A Parent's and Teacher's Handbook for Increasing Awareness

Helping Children
ffected by Abuse

G.W. Medical Publishing, Inc.
St. Louis

This book is dedicated to Dr. Deborah A. Frank, professor of pediatrics at Boston University School of Medicine and director of the Grow Clinic for Children at Boston Medical Center. In addition to being a mom, she has found the time to be a leader in the field of pediatrics, consistently raising awareness of children's developmental needs. Dr. Frank has mentored scores of colleagues by teaching the simple message that children thrive when raised within families and communities that pay very close attention to the nurturing that is every child's right.

A Parent's and Teacher's Handbook for Increasing Awareness

Helping Children

Affected by Abuse

Angelo P. Giardino, MD, PhD, MPH, FAAP
Medical Director
Texas Children's Health Plan
Clinical Associate Professor of Pediatrics
Baylor College of Medicine
Attending Physician
Children's Assessment Center
Texas Children's Hospital
Houston, Texas

RENNER LEARNING RE SOURCE CENTER
ELGIN COMMUNIT Y COLLEGE
ELGIN, ILLINOIS 60123

G.W. Medical Publishing, Inc.
St. Louis

Publishers: Glenn E. Whaley and Marianne V. Whaley

Design Director: Glenn E. Whaley

Managing Editors: Karen C. Maurer
　　　　　　　　Megan O. Hayes

Associate Editors: Robert Lewis
　　　　　　　　Christine Bauer

Book Design/Page Layout: G.W. Graphics
　　　　　　　　　　Charles J. Seibel, III
　　　　　　　　　　Sudon Choe

Print/Production Coordinator: Charles J. Seibel, III

Cover Design: G.W. Graphics

Color Prepress Specialist: G.W. Graphics
　　　　　　　　　　Charles J. Seibel, III

Developmental Editor: Karen C. Maurer

Copy Editor: Dave M. Dumas

Proofreader: Michael S. McConnell

Indexer: Robert A. Saigh

Publisher:
G.W. Medical Publishing, Inc.
77 Westport Plaza, Suite 366, St. Louis, Missouri, 63146-3124 U.S.A.
Phone: (314) 542-4213 Fax: (314) 542-4239 Toll Free: 1-800-600-0330
http://www.gwmedical.com

Library of Congress Cataloging-in-Publication Data

Helping children affected by abuse : a parent and teacher's handbook for increasing awareness / [edited by] Angelo P. Giardino.
　　p. cm.
　Includes bibliographical references and index.
　ISBN-13: 978-1-878060-98-3
　ISBN-10: 1-878060-98-8
　1. Child abuse--United States. 2. Child abuse--United States--Prevention. I. Giardino, Angelo P.
　HV6626.2.H45 2007
　362.760973--dc22
　　　　　　　　2006034699

CONTRIBUTORS

Eileen R. Giardino, PhD, RN, APRN, FNP
Associate Professor of Nursing
The University of Texas School of Nursing at Houston
Department of Acute & Continuing Care
Houston, Texas

Maria D. McColgan, MD, MEd, FAAP
Director
Child Protection Program
St. Christopher's Hospital for Children
Assistant Professor
Drexel University College of Medicine
Philadelphia, Pennsylvania

Peggy S. Tuter Pearl, EdD
Professor of Child and Family Development
Missouri State University
Springfield, Missouri

Kay Stovall, MA, MFT, ATR-BC
Director, Graduate Art Therapy Program
Associate Professor of Clinical Psychiatry and Behavioral Sciences
Eastern Virginia Medical School
Norfolk, Virginia

Elizabeth A. Warson, MA, ATR-BC, LPC
Assistant Professor
Graduate Art Therapy Program
Eastern Virginia Medical School
Norfolk, Virginia

FOREWORD

I am honored to write a foreword for Dr. Angelo Giardino's important text, *Helping Children Affected by Abuse: A Parent's and Teacher's Handbook for Increasing Awareness*. As a developmentalist and a parent, the value of this work is apparent to me on many levels. Raising awareness of the many aspects of child maltreatment is the most basic, but most essential, step in preventing child abuse and neglect.

All too often, we read, see, and hear reports of horrific, long-term abuse that went unnoticed by those charged with children's care, such as neighbors, friends, and teachers. Recently, in my home state of Massachusetts, a case of extreme medical neglect nearly resulting in death emerged in the media, as did the case of a child who was being prostituted so that her mother could support a drug addiction. The investigation of each case revealed that many risk factors and signs of the maltreatment had existed, but none were recognized by the other adults in contact with the children. Could an increase in awareness of the correlates of abuse and neglect lead to the prevention of this kind of terrible mistreatment? Quite possibly, yes.

This book breaks the jargon of child protective services and the medical community down into terms that a lay audience can understand. It is my suspicion that more cases of maltreatment might have been caught earlier had this information been more readily accessible in the past.

This handbook proposes some ambitious societal strategies to address the prevention of child maltreatment. Although it would take major change to achieve prevention on this level, it seems that the goal of this text—raising awareness of abuse on the individual level—may be the first step toward such change. By breaking down the indicators of abuse for a lay audience, this book provides a real service to our society as a whole.

The text also is valuable in that it provides concrete strategies that parents can use to positively discipline their children and choose a supplementary caregiver, while at the same time educating all on the risks for, signs of, and effects of maltreatment of any kind. It is especially important that those who come into frequent contact with children understand these risks and are able to work with parents to prevent abuse and neglect. This book provides the groundwork for this critical step in the prevention of child abuse and neglect and will help us protect our children from ourselves and others.

Anne E. Brady, PhD
Research Assistant Professor
Eliot-Pearson Department of Child Development
Tufts University
Medford, Massachusetts

FOREWORD

Helping Children Affected by Abuse, written by health care personnel, exists for the sole purpose of protecting our children. We have made tremendous gains in the treatment and prevention of childhood disease, yet physical, emotional, and sexual abuse of children persists unchecked. Physicians have traditionally focused on the outcomes of abuse; it is only recently that we have tried preventing abuse, an effort for which we must also enlist the help of parents, teachers, and the general public. Hence this book.

We are pediatricians, one in mid career, the other in training, with perhaps a more personal than professional interest in this book. We both have children, some already in adulthood, and we have discovered that we have made similar observations about raising our children. For example:

"I remember those very trying times when my children's demands triggered frustration, and sometimes also anger. Was it the pediatrician in me that allowed me to understand their needs, tolerate their demands, and calm down? Would I have acted differently, perhaps violently, if it were not for my own educational and parental training?"

"I am a pediatrician-in-training with a toddler-aged daughter, and I am learning every day how much aggravation is a part of parenthood. Recently, my daughter, who is not allowed to stand in the bathtub during her bath, stood up anyway. 'Sit down,' I said, and she sat, smiled, and immediately stood again. 'Sit DOWN,' I repeated, plopping her back into the water. Again she stood, this time with the challenging chirp, 'Up!' It was not that this scene continued for the next 20 minutes, it was that we had already gone through it 5 times that week. Is it any wonder children get hurt by parents who are unable to redirect mounting frustration and anger? I know that a toddler's job is to challenge the rules and that my daughter's stubborn misbehavior is a sign of normal development. So why is it sometimes so difficult to find a growing child charming?"

As adults, we generally interact with a certain degree of restraint, respect, and common sense while simultaneously enduring life's stresses. Add the unrelenting, and seemingly selfish, demands of children to these stresses, or the more significant issues of mental illness and lack of emotional or financial support, and we can see how and why child abuse happens. Can we, as a community, prevent child abuse if parents and caregivers are taught to understand children better, to see what circumstances can trigger abuse, and to prevent those circumstances from occurring?

This book is for parents, teachers, and the general public to learn about the many forms of abuse, how abuse may manifest in school or in childcare, and how legal, mental, social, and civic programs can help prevent abuse. We hope that the reader will learn to recognize vulnerable children and dangerous situations before abuse occurs and take positive steps, such as initiating parenting education, coping skills training, social services involvement, or even family restructuring, before the damage is done.

Joseph A. Zenel, MD
Associate Professor and Vice Chair, Clinical Affairs Pediatrics
Doernbecher Children's Hospital
Oregon Health & Science University
Portland, Oregon

Kerry McGee, MD
Third-Year Resident, Pediatrics
Doernbecher Children's Hospital
Oregon Health & Science University
Portland, Oregon

PREFACE

Over the years, parents and other caregivers struggling with the aftermath of child maltreatment have asked me to recommend a friendly, practical resource that would provide them with easy access to information on child abuse and neglect. After collaborating with G.W. Medical Publishing on many publications for professionals, it was a refreshing change to work on a book that would help the adults most directly involved in caring for children.

I have tried to organize the book in a straightforward manner, and I chose content using the many questions parents and even some of my medical colleagues typically ask when they are concerned that a child is at risk for being harmed. These questions include:

— What exactly are child abuse and neglect?

— How common are child physical abuse, sexual abuse, and neglect?

— Who are these abusers, and how do I know if my children are at risk?

— How do I talk to my child about sexual abuse?

— What can I do if my child is being harmed by abuse or neglect? How can I cope?

— How can I help if I know someone else's child is being or has been abused?

These questions and others are thoroughly answered in the chapters of this book. Other topics addressed are safe discipline techniques, Internet safety issues, choosing quality childcare, and, in situations where a child is a victim, mental health concerns and types of therapy. Each chapter is arranged in a format that makes information easy to retrieve, and the practical facts and friendly tone will allow parents and caregivers to rely on it as an everyday guide to child maltreatment and what they can do about it.

I would like to express my thanks to peer reviewers Noemi Montejo and Sherri Henry, who read every page of this book and offered comments on how to make the material most relevant to the families, teachers, and other caregivers who will be reading it.

It is my hope that with this book, parents, teachers, nurses, and other adults will have the knowledge to identify and prevent the abuse and neglect of the children in their care. Although the ultimate goal is that no child is ever abused or neglected, for now I hope this book can help build a society that cares for and protects all children, and works toward sparing future generations from this devastating problem.

Angelo P. Giardino, MD, PhD, MPH, FAAP

REVIEWS

This book successfully addresses the complexity of all forms of child maltreatment including the scope and nature, causes, and consequences of physical abuse, sexual abuse, emotional abuse, and neglect. The focus is on diagnosis, intervention, and prevention, enhancing the roles of the healthcare provider to become more engaged with families and effective community-based programs that can help these children and their parents. There are excellent examples of intervention and prevention strategies for both parents and teachers to utilize for children and their caregivers. The authors have added three important sections on timely areas of concern: the parameters and key issues surrounding dating violence, childcare settings, and Internet safety. Additionally, an overview of public child welfare, mental health, and team decision making are reviewed to give the reader a broader understanding of systemic responses to the problem of child abuse and neglect. Also, an introspective chapter on art therapy gives insight into the power of this technique to explore feelings and assist in the healing process for families. A must-read for professionals in the field, teachers, health care providers, and parents alike.

Lisa Pion-Berlin, Ph.D.
President and Chief
Executive Officer
Parents Anonymous® Inc.
Strengthening Families
All Around the World

This well-written volume provides an up-to-date review and analysis of the core topics related to child maltreatment. It delves below the surface to disentangle risk factors for maltreatment from consequences and provides readers with an enhanced understanding of this complex issue. With a focus on prevention and early intervention, this book offers concrete strategies that parents, teachers, and clinicians can employ to respond effectively in situations where abuse is suspected. This book is a valuable resource for anyone working with children.

Catherine Bradshaw, PhD
Assistant Professor
Department of Mental Health
Associate Director
Johns Hopkins Center for the
Prevention of Youth Violence
Johns Hopkins Bloomberg School of
Public Health

The authors have created an excellent overview of child abuse, indicating how child abuse is manifested, how to recognize and treat child abuse, and importantly, how to prevent child abuse for future generations. This is a terrific resource for all individuals who care for children and want to keep them free from harm.

Nancy Chandler
Executive Director
National Children's Alliance

The book is an excellent resource for parents, teachers, and even child protection workers. Dr. Giardino has the ability to simplify complex topics of abuse and make them understandable for both parents and professionals. The book's practical suggestions and guidance on the spectrum of abuse, protecting children, the Internet, schools, and childcare will be indispensable to concerned caregivers and education professionals. The easy language of this book makes it a valuable resource for any personal, professional, or school library.

Michael L Haney, PhD, NCC,
CCISM, LMHC
Division Director for Prevention and
Intervention
Children's Medical Services
Florida Department of Health

This resource book provides a concise and up-to-date look at the complex issues surrounding child abuse. It is a valuable combination of definitions, dynamics and concrete discussions that explore how effective parenting can help prevent child abuse, how teachers can shape the dialogue concerning abuse issues, and how physicians and other professionals can influence positive parenting and prevention efforts. It clearly portrays the responsibility we each have for all the children in our sphere of influence and how we can put that responsibility into action in a variety of contexts. From parents to schools to communities, this book lays out a mandate for protection of children, even as we teach them how to protect themselves. Helping Children Affected by Abuse *is a must have for every school and professional library.*

Sherryll Krazier, PhD
Founder of the Safe Child Program
Author of The Safe Child Book *and*
Bully Proof Your Child

As a medical student interested in public health, and specifically in protecting children from violence, I am always searching for resources to effectively educate communities about "helping children affected by abuse." This book beautifully demonstrates that adults in our society have the responsibility and capacity to protect children. It accomplishes a very important goal of not only outlining different kinds of abuse in a clear and thorough manner, but also providing suggestions of what parents, teachers, and any other adults in a community can do to protect children from the harms of abuse. I think that anyone who interacts with children should have to read Helping Children Affected by Abuse.

Sarah Bagley
Third-Year Medical Student
Georgetown University

G.W. Medical Publishing, Inc.
St. Louis

OUR MISSION

To become the world leader in publishing and

information services on child abuse, maltreatment,

diseases, and domestic violence. We seek to

heighten awareness of these issues and provide

relevant information to professionals and consumers.

A portion of our profits is contributed to nonprofit organizations
dedicated to the prevention of child abuse and the care of victims of abuse
and other children and family charities.

CONTENTS

A Parent's and Teacher's Handbook for Increasing Awareness

Helping Children
Affected by Abuse

G.W. Medical Publishing, Inc.
St. Louis

Chapter 1

Child Abuse and Neglect: An Overview of the Problem

Angelo P. Giardino, MD, PhD, MPH, FAAP

Child abuse and neglect (sometimes referred to by the more general term *child maltreatment*) is a complex problem that affects every segment of society, exempting no social, ethnic, religious, or professional group. The term "abuse" refers to physical, sexual, or psychological injury to a child caused by a parent, babysitter, neighbor, teacher, coach, or some other trusted older person or adult who is in a caregiving role. Child maltreatment can result from acts of commission or omission and is a major public health and social problem facing children and families in the United States and other countries.

Definitions

The US federal government provides a set of definition guidelines for child maltreatment that provide a minimum foundation for states to follow when creating their own laws and regulations.[1] These guidelines recognize maltreatment as:

— Any recent act or failure to act on the part of a parent or caretaker that results in death, serious physical or emotional harm, sexual abuse, or exploitation.

— An act or failure to act that presents an imminent risk of serious harm.

Specific laws vary from state to state—some are very detailed while others are more general—but each makes harming a child in one's care a crime.

"Child abuse and neglect" and "child maltreatment" are general terms that can be broken into the following subcategories, which are briefly described in **Table 1-1**:

— Physical abuse

— Sexual abuse

— Emotional abuse

— Neglect

Size of the Problem

In the United States, national collections of state-reported data consistently find that approximately 3 million reports per year of suspected child maltreatment are made to child protective services (CPS) agencies after processing and investigation, between about 900 000 and 1 million children are found to have been maltreated.[3] Each year, more than half of the confirmed (substantiated) child maltreatment cases are neglect, approximately 20% are physical abuse, 10% are sexual abuse, and the remainder

---

Table 1-1. Forms of Child Abuse and Neglect

Type of Maltreatment	Definition
Physical abuse	Physical injury ranging from minor bruises to broken bones, brain damage, or death that results from a caregiver beating, shaking, throwing, choking, or otherwise harming a child. These injuries are considered abuse regardless of whether the caregiver intended to hurt the child.
Sexual abuse	Sexual activities between a dominant or more powerful person and a dependent, developmentally immature child for the dominant person's sexual stimulation or for the gratification of other persons, as in child pornography or prostitution. The activities defined by child sexual abuse include exhibitionism, inappropriate viewing of the child, allowing the child to view inappropriate sexual material, taking sexual photographs of the child, sexualized kissing, fondling, masturbation, penetration of the vagina or anus with objects or fingers, and oral-genital, genital-genital, and anal-genital contact.
Emotional/ psychological abuse	A pattern of behavior that impairs a child's emotional development or sense of self-worth. This behavior may include constant criticism, threats, or rejection, as well as withholding love, support, or guidance.
Neglect	Failure to provide for a child's basic needs in one or more of the following different forms: — *Physical.* Failure to provide necessary food, clothing, or shelter. — *Medical.* Failure to provide necessary medical, dental, or mental health treatment. — *Educational.* Failure to enroll a child in school, allowing excessive absences from school, or disregarding special educational needs. — *Supervisional.* Lack of appropriate supervision or leaving the child in the custody of others for extended periods of time. — *Emotional.* Inattention to a child's emotional needs, failure to provide psychological care, or permitting the child to engage in risky activities such as permitting access to alcohol or other drugs.

Data from Child Welfare Information Gateway.[2]

---

encompass various other forms of child abuse and neglect. National child maltreatment statistics are released every 2 to 3 years, and, based on the 2004 data, the following observations may be made[3]:

— An estimated 3 million referrals involving 5.5 million children were made to CPS agencies.

— Approximately 63% of the referrals were viewed as serious enough to be "screened in" and accepted for investigation; thus, 37% were screened out and not accepted for investigation.

— Approximately 872 000 children were found to be victims of child abuse or neglect.

— Approximately 1500 children were known to have died as a result of maltreatment.

In 2004, 48% of victims were boys and 52% were girls.[3] The youngest children have the highest victimization rates: children aged 1 to 3 years have a rate of 16.1 per 1000 children, whereas those in the oldest age group (16 to 17 years old) have a rate of only a 6.1 per 1000 children.[3] Approximately 7% of all victims had mental, emotional, behavioral, or physical disabilities, though they are considered undercounted.[3]

More than three quarters of perpetrators of child maltreatment are parents.[3] About 7% of perpetrators are other relatives, and 4% are partners of single parents. Women make up a larger percentage of perpetrators than men—58% are female and 42% are male. This could be because mothers and female caregivers spend more time with children overall than do fathers and other males and thus have more access and exposure to children.

CAUSES OF CHILD ABUSE AND NEGLECT

No single cause or specific predisposing factor has been identified that consistently explains why child abuse and neglect occurs. Some people say understanding the cause of child maltreatment is similar to understanding how a puzzle fits together: there are a lot of pieces that, when combined, fit together to make a picture. However, seeing the whole picture requires all of the pieces, and some pieces play a larger role than others.

The scientific model that explains a lot of the situations that give rise to abuse is called the *human ecological model*. Human ecological studies of child abuse and neglect describe how parenting styles and abilities, family functioning dynamics, environmental factors, and child-related characteristics combine to create a set of circumstances in which child maltreatment can occur. The human ecological model sees a child as functioning within a family (microsystem), the family as functioning within a community (exosystem), and various communities as linked together by a set of sociocultural values that exert an influence upon them (macrosystem). **Figure 1-1** shows the child and family existing at the center of these interacting systems. **Table 1-2** summarizes these various factors and characteristics as they relate to a human ecological view of child abuse and neglect. Since the human ecological model does not explain sexual abuse as well as physical abuse and neglect, scientists have developed other models to explain sexual abuse specifically (see Chapter 3, Child Sexual Abuse).

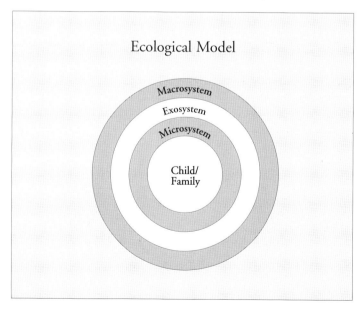

Figure 1-1. *Model showing how the child functions within other systems. Data from Bronfenbrenner.*[4]

Table 1-2. Types of Factors and Characteristics Useful in a Human Ecological View of Child Abuse and Neglect

FACTOR/ CHARACTERISTIC	EXAMPLE	DISCUSSION
Parent or Caregiver	**Personality/ psychology**	Although no specific set of characteristics consistently exists in all abusive caregivers, characteristics frequently identified in physically abusive or neglectful caregivers include: — Low self-esteem — Belief that events are determined by chance or by outside forces beyond one's control — Poor impulse control — Depression, anxiety, and antisocial behavior
	History of maltreatment	Caregivers with poor parental role models may find it difficult to implement positive parenting practices with their own children. Children who experience maltreatment or witness violence between their parents or caregivers may learn to justify violent behavior as appropriate. Although some who were maltreated will subject their children to maltreatment, it is incorrect to assume that a maltreated child will always grow up to become a maltreating parent.
	Substance abuse	Substance abuse is a contributing factor for a large number of maltreating caregivers.
	Attitudes and knowledge	Poor understanding about child development and negative views about a child's behavior may contribute to child maltreatment. Abusive caregivers may exhibit the following qualities: — Significantly lower or higher than normal expectations for children's behavior — Less accurate understanding of appropriate developmental stages
	Age	Caregivers who are younger exhibit higher rates of child abuse than do older caregivers.
Family Factors	**Family size and structure**	Single-parent households and households with more children and/or more people may be at higher risk of child maltreatment.
	Domestic violence (also known as intimate partner violence)	In violent homes, children may: — Be victims of physical abuse. — Witness parental violence. — Be neglected because the caregivers are overly focused on the other partner's behavior or are unresponsive to them due to pervasive fear of violence.
	Stress	Physical abuse has been associated with stressful life events, parenting stress, and emotional distress.

(continued)

Table 1-2. *(continued)*

FACTOR/ CHARACTERISTIC	EXAMPLE	DISCUSSION
Family Factors	**Stress**	Caregivers who maltreat often experience or believe they are experiencing high levels of stress. Examples of stressful situations include physical illness, losing a job, marital problems, and the death of a family member.
	Caregiver-child interaction	Caregivers who maltreat tend to be less supportive of, affectionate with, playful with, and responsive to their children. Abusive caregivers may be more likely to use harsh disciplinary strategies, such as hitting, prolonged isolation, and verbal aggression and less likely to use positive parenting strategies, such as time-outs, reasoning, and recognizing and encouraging the child's successes.
Child Factors	**Disabilities**	Children with physical, cognitive, and emotional disabilities are at nearly twice the risk of being maltreated as children without disabilities. Reasons thought to explain this increased risk include: — Children being perceived by their parents as "different" because of their special needs. — Overwhelming caregiving needs being required. — Disruptions occurring in the bonding process due to frequent hospitalizations or children's inability to respond to affection. — Children, due to developmental limitations, lacking the maturity or judgement to understand behaviors typically considered imappropriate or being unable to escape abusive situations.
Environmental Factors	**Social isolation**	Isolation may contribute to or become a consequence of maltreatment. "Isolated caregivers" are those who perceive or actually have less material and emotional support, sometimes lack positive parenting role models, and/or feel less pressure to conform to conventional caregiving standards. These conditions are especially true for immigrant families who may not have any other family members in this country and are faced with obstacles such language barriers, lack of knowledge of existing resources, limited means of transportation, and limited avenues for other interaction.
	Poverty	Poverty may exacerbate other risk factors, such as depression, substance abuse, and social isolation, thereby increasing the risk for child abuse and neglect.

Data from Goldman et al.[5]

HOW TO RECOGNIZE WHEN A CHILD IS BEING ABUSED OR NEGLECTED

It is important to recognize the signs of child maltreatment, which are observable in both the child and the caregiver. **Table 1-3** lists some of the signs that may indicate a child is being abused or neglected.

Table 1-3. Signs of Child Maltreatment

FORM OF MALTREATMENT	CONSIDER CHILD MALTREATMENT WHEN THE CHILD . . .	CONSIDER CHILD MALTREATMENT WHEN THE PARENT OR OTHER ADULT CAREGIVER . . .
Physical abuse	— Has unexplained burns, bites, bruises, broken bones, or black eyes. — Has fading bruises or other marks noticeable after an absence from school. — Seems afraid of parents or caregivers; protests or cries when it is time to go home. — Shrinks at the approach of adults. — Reports an injury caused by a parent or caregiver.	— Offers conflicting, unconvincing, or no explanation for the child's injury. — Describes the child as "evil" or in some other very negative way. — Uses harsh physical discipline with the child. — Has a history of abuse as a child.
Sexual abuse	— Has a sudden change in behavior or attitude. — Has trouble sleeping or undergoes a change in sleep pattern. — Experiences a sudden change in appetite. — Demonstrates bizarre or sophisticated sexual knowledge or behavior. — Has difficulty walking or sitting. — Becomes pregnant or contracts a sexually transmitted disease, particularly if younger than 14 years. — Runs away. — Reports sexual abuse by a parent or caregiver.	— Is unduly protective of the child or severely limits the child's contact with other children, especially those of the opposite sex. — Is secretive and isolated. — Is jealous or controlling with family members.
Emotional abuse	— Shows extremes in behavior, such as being overly compliant, demanding, passive, or aggressive. — Acts inappropriately adult-like (parenting other children) or inappropriately infantile (frequently rocking or head-banging). — Is delayed in physical or emotional development. — Has attempted suicide. — Reports a lack of attachment to the parent.	— Constantly blames, belittles, or berates the child. — Is unconcerned about the child and refuses to consider offers of help for the child's problems. — Constantly rejects the child.

(continued)

Table 1-3. *(continued)*		
FORM OF MALTREATMENT	CONSIDER CHILD MALTREATMENT WHEN THE CHILD . . .	CONSIDER CHILD MALTREATMENT WHEN THE PARENT OR OTHER ADULT CAREGIVER . . .
Neglect	— Is frequently absent from school. — Begs for or steals food or money. — Lacks needed medical or dental care, immunizations, or glasses. — Is consistently dirty and has severe body odor. — Lacks sufficient clothing for the weather. — Abuses alcohol or other drugs. — States that there is no one at home to provide care.	— Appears to be indifferent to the child. — Seems apathetic or depressed. — Behaves irrationally or in a bizarre manner. — Is abusing alcohol or other drugs.

Data from Child Welfare Information Gateway.[6]

PROFESSIONAL RESPONSE

Professionals such as doctors, nurses, and teachers are required by state law in all 50 states to report suspicions of child maltreatment to the proper governmental authorities. Most states require notification be made to the CPS agency, some require notification of the police, and others require notification of both.

Because members of the above-listed professions are required to report their suspicions of child maltreatment, they are referred to as *mandated reporters*. However, mandated reporters are not the only ones who can make such reports. Parents and concerned adults, even if they are not required by law to report child maltreatment, may voluntarily do so. In fact, only an estimated 56% of all reports are made by mandated reporters (**Figure 1-2**).[3]

The laws regarding mandated reporters are changing over time. According to the Child Welfare Information Gateway, as of April 2006, approximately 18 states are moving beyond only considering professionals as mandated reporters and now require any person, regardless of occupation, who suspects child abuse or neglect to report it.[7] Professionals who fail to make a report of suspected abuse may be held liable under the state's law and could face both criminal and civil consequences.

"Suspicion of abuse" is established when information leads a competent professional or adult to conclude that child abuse or neglect is likely to have occurred. Reporting adults do not have to actually prove that abuse or neglect has occurred, nor must they determine the identity of the abuser. CPS, the police, and the court system are responsible for those tasks. Furthermore, if it is later discovered that no maltreatment has occurred, the reporting adult cannot be prosecuted for making an incorrect report, even if a caregiver files a lawsuit against them. Under state law, as long as a report was made in good faith, its reporter can claim immunity from criminal and civil liability. "Good faith" implies that no motive existed for the report beyond an interest in protecting a child from possible abuse and that the information reported was believed to be accurate at the time of the report.

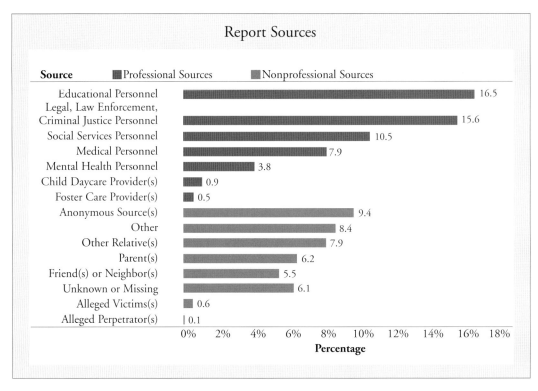

Figure 1-2. Percentages of reports received by source, broken into professional and nonprofessional categories. Reprinted from USDHHS.[3]

Once a report is made, usually in the form of a call to the state or county hotline followed by some form of written documentation, the state laws outline a timeline for the subsequent evaluation. CPS will screen the information, conduct an investigation, and provide support services for the child and family. CPS is typically focused on the safety of the child and the functioning and well-being of the family involved. The police may also become involved, depending on the circumstances of the case. They focus on the criminal aspects of the case and often work in cooperation with CPS during the investigation. **Figure 1-3** provides a schematic of how CPS typically responds to a case of suspected child maltreatment.

AFTER SUSPECTED CHILD ABUSE OR NEGLECT IS REPORTED

A number of options are available to CPS if a case is determined to involve child maltreatment. In cases where the risk of further abuse is considered very low, CPS may "close" the case. If needed, CPS may help the family get connected to helpful services through a variety of social support systems available in the family's community.

In situations in which the risk is seen as low to moderate, CPS will typically stay involved and arrange for community-based or voluntary in-home services. They will supervise the family and monitor the members' participation. Services will continue until CPS determines that the risk of abuse has decreased or that additional interventions are necessary—especially if the family fails to cooperate. In some cases, CPS may offer the family services as a social support even if no abuse or neglect is substantiated.

In more difficult situations, when risk to children is moderate to high, CPS may again offer the family voluntary in-home services. If these are refused, CPS then seeks court intervention to force the family to comply with whatever services are deemed necessary

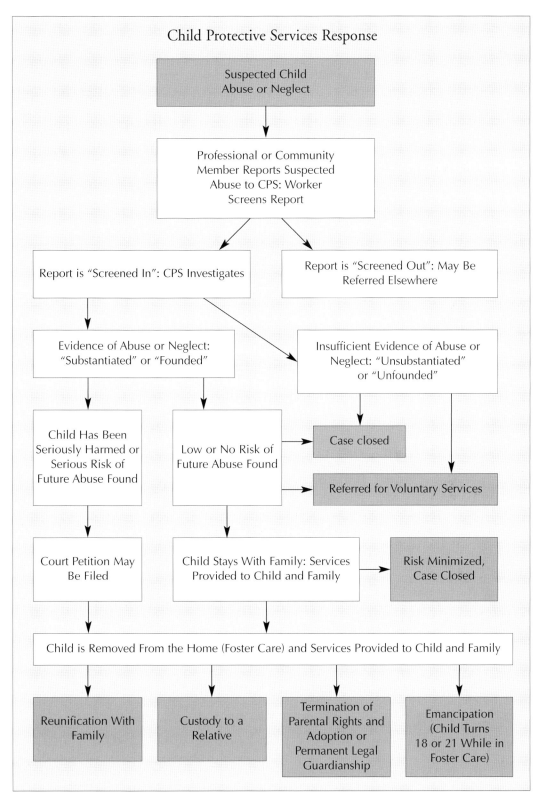

Figure 1-3. *Flow of how CPS responds to reports of child maltreatment. Reprinted from Child Welfare Information Gateway.*[7]

for the children's protection. Once the court determines that abuse or neglect has occurred, families will be required to participate with in-home CPS services. These services will continue as long as a family participates and the court believes that children can remain safely at home.

If a child has been seriously harmed or is considered to be at high risk of serious harm from future maltreatment, the court may order the child's removal from the home. The child may then be temporarily placed in the care of a relative, called *kinship care*, or in the care of someone not related to them, called *foster care*. In 2004, an estimated 268 000 children in the United States were removed from their homes after CPS investigation.[3] In any given year, approximately 550 000 children are in foster care.[8] On average, children placed in foster care remain in the system for about 12 months, and approximately 50% return to their parents.[9] Federal laws require courts to hold a "permanency hearing" within 12 months of a child's entrance into the system in order to determine the permanent placement plan for the child. Long-term care in a foster care setting, which was quite common in previous decades, has been dramatically reduced. Children today are either returned to their original families as soon as safely possible or adopted. Courts typically conduct reviews of each child's case on a fairly frequent basis to ensure that CPS is actively developing and implementing a permanency plan for each child.

IMPACT OF CHILD ABUSE AND NEGLECT

The impact of child abuse and neglect is often discussed in terms of separate physical, psychological, behavioral, and societal consequences, as if there is no overlap among these categories. However, these consequences are actually quite interrelated, and it is impossible to separate them completely. For example, physical damage to a child's growing brain can have psychological consequences, causing cognitive delays or emotional difficulties that can in turn result in poor scholastic performance or problematic social relationships. Related psychological problems may also lead to risk-taking behaviors: A teenager who is depressed or experiencing anxiety may be more likely to smoke, abuse alcohol or illicit drugs, or overeat. Furthermore, harmful behaviors and decision-making strategies that begin in childhood might turn into long-term physical health problems, such as sexually transmitted diseases, cancer, or obesity.[10]

Just as there is no single cause of child maltreatment, there is no standard or consistent outcome. Results of individual cases vary widely and are affected by a combination of factors, which can include:

— The child's age and developmental needs during the period of the maltreatment.

— The relationship of the child to the abuser.

— The response of the nonabusing adults in the child's environment after the abuse comes to light.

— The type, frequency, duration, and severity of the maltreatment.

The impact of maltreatment on a child's physical health ranges from minor injuries that heal rapidly to more severe injuries that may heal but have scarring or long-term effects. For example, a significant burn may heal but cause obvious disfigurement. In some cases of child abuse and neglect, the timing and severity of the injuries can lead to impaired brain development that will permanently affect the child's physical, mental, and social functioning. The child will not develop to his or her original potential, may perform poorly in school, and may have difficulty connecting with other people as a result. Among the most severe forms of child abuse and neglect is abusive head trauma, at times referred to as "shaken baby syndrome" (SBS), which occurs when a caregiver shakes a child so violently that the nerves in the child's brain are damaged. Immediate effects of SBS include vomiting, trouble breathing, difficulty being aroused from sleep, seizures, or, in extreme cases, even death. Children who survive injury from violent shaking commonly suffer blindness, learning difficulties, paralysis, and damage to a variety of other sensory and motor functions. The physical impact of child maltreatment may not be limited to childhood; emerging evidence suggests that there is a relationship between living in a violent family setting as a child: and long-term health problems in adulthood, such as heart disease, cancer, lung disease, and liver disease.[11,12]

The impact of child maltreatment on psychological health and well-being is the easiest to understand. Immediate psychological effects include feelings of fear, isolation, and mistrust. These effects can become long-standing and lead to anxiety, depression, low self-esteem, and difficulty establishing and maintaining interpersonal relationships. Many maltreated children have various diagnosable psychological problems as they grow older, including attention-deficit/hyperactivity disorder, posttraumatic stress disorder, anxiety, panic disorder, eating disorders, depression, reactive attachment disorder, dissociative disorders, and suicidal tendencies.[13,14] These potential psychological effects are related to a number of behavioral effects: at least one fourth of victimized children also experience teenaged pregnancy, poor school performance, juvenile delinquency (severe enough that the police become involved), and substance abuse.[15]

Finally, society bears a tremendous financial cost related to child maltreatment. Direct costs, which include all of the expenses for health care, CPS investigation, police investigation, and the courts, have been estimated to exceed $24 billion per year.[16] Estimated indirect costs to society are $69 billion a year—nearly 3 times the direct costs—and include the expense of increased physical and mental health care for the child and family over a lifetime, the various costs of juvenile and adult criminal activity, and all expenses associated with increased substance abuse and domestic violence. Other indirect costs include loss of productivity due to unemployment and underemployment and the expense of special education for the victims of child abuse and neglect.[10]

FOCUS ON PREVENTION

Most people who are concerned with the well-being of children share a commitment to seeing the end of all child maltreatment. In order to realize this dream, Prevent Child Abuse America (PCA America), a national organization whose mission is to effectively promote prevention efforts at all levels of society, suggests an approach to the problem that begins with awareness building and then moves to specific actions.[17] Increased awareness of child maltreatment increases basic understanding of its underlying and related issues, and reading books such as this is one way to stimulate awareness. In addition, PCA America suggests that interested citizens take concrete steps to become involved in the child abuse and neglect prevention effort. **Table 1-4** provides examples of how to become involved in stopping this major problem facing children.

Table 1-4. Steps for Getting Involved in the Prevention of Child Abuse and Neglect	
Get involved with family support programs	Parent education, community centers, respite care services, and substance abuse treatment programs help to protect children by addressing circumstances that place families at risk for child abuse and neglect. Donate your time or money if you can.
	(continued)

Table 1-4. *(continued)*	
Report suspected child abuse and neglect	Some states require everyone to report suspected abuse or neglect; others specify members of certain professions, such as educators and doctors. But whether you are mandated by law to report child abuse and neglect, doing so may save a child. If you suspect a child is being abused or neglected, call the police or your local child welfare agency.
Spread the word	Help educate others in your community about child abuse and neglect. Ask if you can leave a stack of brochures at your local public library, recreation center, community center, government center, or other public place. You also might make material available at your church, synagogue, mosque, temple, or other faith institution.
Strengthen the fabric of your community	Know your neighbors' names and the names of their children, and make sure they know yours. Give stressed parents a break by offering to watch their children. Volunteer. If you like interacting with children, great, but you do not have to volunteer directly with kids to contribute to prevention. All activities that strengthen communities, such as service to civic clubs and participation on boards and committees, ultimately contribute to the well-being of children.
Be ready in an emergency	We have all witnessed the screaming-child-in-the-supermarket scenario. If we are parents, at least once that screaming child has been ours. Most parents take the typical tantrum in stride. But what if you witness a scene in which you believe a child is being, or is about to be, physically or verbally abused? Responding in these circumstances technically moves beyond prevention and into intervention, and intervention is best handled by professionals. If you find yourself in this situation, consider the following steps: — Talk to the adult to get his or her attention away from the child. Be friendly. — Say something like, "Children can really wear you out, can't they?" or "My child has done the same thing." — Ask if you can help in any way—could you carry some packages? Play with an older child so the baby can be fed or changed? Call someone on your cell phone? — If you see a child alone in a public place—for example, unattended in a grocery cart—stay with the child until the parent returns.

Data from NCCAN.[18]

PCA America reminds us that prevention begins at home and requires self-reflection and a commitment to action. Parents and caregivers must take time to reevaluate their caregiving skills with honesty and frankness. It is never too late to take a parenting class, pick up a book on child development, or ask friends or colleagues who seem especially good at caregiving for suggestions or ideas on ways to improve.

CONCLUSION

Child abuse and neglect is a major problem facing children and families. The large numbers of reports and ultimately substantiated cases illustrates how pervasive this problem is for our children. The negative impact that physical, sexual, or emotional injury can have on children is staggering and demands attention. Consequences of physical injuries are clear, and the hidden impacts of sexual and emotional victimization are equally as damaging. The need for an effective response goes beyond what CPS and the police are required to do: It requires individuals and communities to assess what resources they have to direct toward this problem, raise awareness of it, and help build resources so that cases of abuse are investigated and handled appropriately.

REFERENCES

1. The Federal Child Abuse Prevention and Treatment Act (CAPTA), 42 USCA §5106g, as amended by the Keeping Children and Families Safe Act of 2003. Available at: http://www.acf.hhs.gov/programs/cb/laws_policies/cblaws/capta03/index.htm. Accessed June 27, 2006.

2. Child Welfare Information Gateway. *What Is Child Abuse and Neglect?* Washington, DC: Child Welfare Information Gateway; 2006. Available at: http://www.child welfare.gov/pubs/factsheets/whatiscan.cfm. Accessed June 27, 2006.

3. US Department of Health & Human Services. *Child Maltreatment 2004*. Washington, DC: US Government Printing Office; 2006. Available at: http://www. acf.hhs.gov/programs/cb/pubs/cm04/insidecover.htm. Accessed June 26, 2006.

4. Bronfenbrenner U. *The Ecology of Human Development*. Cambridge, Mass: Harvard University Press; 1979.

5. Goldman J, Salus MK, Wolcott D, Kennedy KY. *A Coordinated Response to Child Abuse and Neglect: The Foundation for Practice*. Washington, DC: US Dept of Health & Human Services; 2003.

6. Child Welfare Information Gateway. *Recognizing Child Abuse and Neglect: Signs and Symptoms*. Washington, DC: Child Welfare Information Gateway; 2006. Available at: http://www.childwelfare.gov/pubs/factsheets/signs.pdf. Accessed June 28, 2006.

7. Child Welfare Information Gateway. *How Does the Child Welfare System Work?* Washington, DC: Child Welfare Information Gateway; 2006. Available at: http://www.childwelfare.gov/pubs/factsheets/cpswork.pdf. Accessed June 27, 2006.

8. American Academy of Pediatrics. *Fostering Health: Health Care for Children and Adolescents in Foster Care*. 2nd ed. Elk Grove Village, Ill: American Academy of Pediatrics; 2004.

9. US Department of Health & Human Services. *The AFCARS Report #9: Preliminary FY 2002 Estimates as of August 2004*. Washington, DC: US Department of Health and Human Services; 2004.

10. Child Welfare Information Gateway. *Long Term Consequences of Child Abuse and Neglect*. Washington, DC: Child Welfare Information Gateway; 2006. Available at: http://www.childwelfare.gov/pubs/factsheets/long_term_consequences.pdf. Accessed June 28, 2006.

11. Felitti VJ, Anda RF, Nordenberg D, et al. Relationship of childhood abuse and household dysfunction to many of the leading causes of death in adults: the adverse childhood experiences (ACE) study. *Am J Prev Med*. 1998;14:245-258.

12. Hillis SD, Anda RF, Felitti VJ, Nordenberg D, Marchbanks PA. Adverse childhood experiences and sexually transmitted diseases in men and women: a retrospective study. *Pediatrics*. 2000:106:e11.

13. Silverman AB, Reinherz HZ, Giaconia RM. The long-term sequelae of child and adolescent abuse: a longitudinal community study. *Child Abuse Negl*. 1996;20:709-723.

14. Teicher MD. Wounds that time won't heal: the neurobiology of child abuse. *Cerebrum*. 2000;2:50-67.

15. Kelley BT, Thornberry TP, Smith CA. *In the Wake of Childhood Maltreatment*. Washington, DC: National Institute of Justice; 1997.

16. Fromm S, for Prevent Child Abuse America. *Total Estimated Cost of Child Abuse and Neglect in the United States*. Chicago, Ill: Prevent Child Abuse America; 2001.

17. Prevent Child Abuse America. *Fact Sheet: An Approach to Preventing Child Abuse*. Chicago, Ill: Prevent Child Abuse America; 2003.

18. National Clearinghouse on Child Abuse & Neglect Information. *You Have the Power to Prevent Child Abuse and Neglect*. Washington, DC: National Clearinghouse on Child Abuse & Neglect Information; 2005. Available at: http://www.childwelfare.gov/pubs/prevenres/tips.pdf. Accessed June 28, 2006.

Chapter 2

PHYSICAL ABUSE

Angelo P. Giardino, MD, PhD, MPH, FAAP

Physical abuse is a subcategory of child maltreatment, accounting for approximately one fifth of all cases. Parents are often most familiar with this type of abuse because its symptoms are the most visible. State laws require some professionals to report suspected physical abuse, but any adult who cares for children should recognize his or her ability—and responsibility—to make voluntary reports. All responsible adults should look for the possible appearance of abusive injuries, know how to differentiate between accidental and abusive injuries, understand the impacts of physical abuse, understand the need to report these suspicions to authorities, and know what to expect if they do report abuse.

DEFINITION

Physical abuse is a situation in which a child is injured while in the care of a parent or other caregiver. These injuries are called inflicted, abusive, or nonaccidental injuries. The US federal government defines physical abuse as a form of maltreatment during which a caregiver inflicts an injury that may be recognized during examination upon a child. This definition includes such various nonaccidental means of injury as hitting with a hand, stick, strap, or other object; shaking; throwing; burning; stabbing; and choking.[1] Some definitions for physical abuse attempt to characterize the *seriousness* of the injury, which can vary anywhere from mild redness that fades over several hours to injuries resulting in death.

Recent medical definitions have paid less attention to the *intention* of the injury and more attention to its actual *effect*. The reason for this shift is to prevent caregivers who have injured their children from acquitting themselves by stating that they did not *intend* to injure the child. What is important today is what actually happened to the child, not what the caregiver intended.

It is easy to diagnose a child who has many injuries inflicted over time; one does not need professional health care training to recognize this pattern. (General signs of abuse are listed in **Table 2-1**.) However, when a child has only a single injury, diagnosis can sometimes be difficult, even for those who are experienced health care professionals. There is a great need to determine whether an injury is accidental or inflicted, for much hangs in the balance. If a child is being intentionally abused but the injury is misdiagnosed as accidental, the child will be left in the care of a person who may cause other intentional injuries. Siblings or other children in the household are also put at risk. On the other hand, if the injury is accidental but mistakenly thought to be intentional, innocent caregivers will be falsely accused and face criminal and civil investigations as well as negative social reactions, all of which can disrupt the family's normal functioning.

SIZE OF THE PROBLEM

In the United States, approximately 872 000 children were maltreated in 2004.[3] Approximately 18% of these cases were identified as physical abuse (**Figure 2-1**).

Table 2-1. Signs of Physical Abuse	
Consider the possibility of physical abuse when the **child:**	— Has unexplained injuries, such as burns, bites, bruises, broken bones, or black eyes. — Has fading bruises or other marks noticeable after an unexpected absence from school. — Seems frightened of the parents and protests or cries when it is time to go home; alternately, appears fearful at the approach of adults in general. — Reports injury by a parent or another adult caregiver.
Consider the possibility of physical abuse when the **parent or caregiver:**	— Offers conflicting, unconvincing, or no explanation for the child's injury. — Describes the child as evil or bad or in some other negative way. — Uses harsh physical discipline with the child.

Data from Prevent Child Abuse America.[2]

Figure 2-1. *In 2004, 17.5% of child maltreatment cases involved physical abuse. Data from USDHHS.*[3]

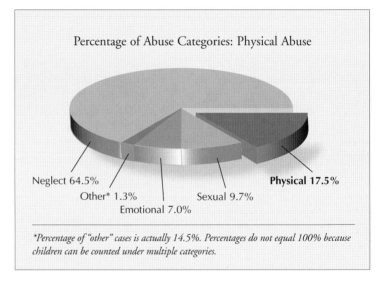

Percentage of Abuse Categories: Physical Abuse

Neglect 64.5%
Other* 1.3%
Emotional 7.0%
Sexual 9.7%
Physical 17.5%

*Percentage of "other" cases is actually 14.5%. Percentages do not equal 100% because children can be counted under multiple categories.

Encouragingly, the rate of victimization per 1000 children in the national population has dropped from 13.4 children in 1990 to 11.9 children in 2004. Many child abuse professionals hope that this decrease is real and will continue in the future due to attention and prevention efforts. However, even if the numbers have already decreased, they still remain high, so efforts to eliminate this problem must continue. Even one child hurt by abuse is one too many.

CAUSES OF PHYSICAL ABUSE

Physical abuse can result from a number of circumstances, such as when:

— Caregivers use corporal punishment and their anger becomes uncontrollable.

— Caregivers lack understanding of appropriate child development and have un-realistic expectations of children, leading to increased stress and situations in which a child's behavior is viewed negatively.

— Caregivers' psychology is such that they resent or reject their child.

— Children are left in the care of babysitters who are abusive.

— Caregivers use substances like alcohol or drugs and then exhibit violent behavior toward children.

— Caregivers live in an environment with domestic violence that entangles children and causes injury.

No single cause has been identified that explains the occurrence of all cases of physical abuse. Understanding the many factors that contribute to physical abuse requires a combination of scientific models to explain various cases.

As discussed in Chapter 1 (Child Abuse and Neglect: An Overview of the Problem), the human ecological model of development and interaction is generally regarded as an ideal conceptual framework from which to approach the complex interactions among a caregiver, child, family, social situation, and cultural values that lead to child abuse. Essentially, various factors related to these elements interact to create a situation where abuse is possible. Several issues related to child abuse and neglect that get a high degree of attention in the human ecological model include stress, caregiver frustration, use of corporal punishment, and the presence of domestic violence.

STRESS AND CAREGIVER FRUSTRATION

A professional study by Dr. Ray Helfer[4] of physical abuse based on the human ecological model describes how physical abuse arises when a caregiver and child interact around an event—often an episode of misbehavior—in a stressful environment. Parents and caregivers have unique personal developmental histories, personality styles, psychological functioning and coping strategies, expectations of children, and levels of ability to nurture. Additionally, children may have certain characteristics that make providing care more complex. Specific factors that may place children at higher risk for physical abuse include prematurity, poor bonding with caregivers, being medically fragile or having various special needs, and being perceived as different or difficult—especially regarding temperament.

An environment may also contain stressors that make parents or caregivers feel less than capable, overextending their baseline coping abilities. There is a statistical link between such environments and increased rates of abuse. Of course, interactions between environmental stress and caregivers' frustration are complex, and not all stressed caregivers respond by inflicting harm upon their children. One factor that seems to play a role in children's risk of being maltreated is the caregivers' level of social interaction with others, including both relatives and nonrelatives. Statistics indicate that as the level of social isolation increases, the risk for maltreatment increases alongside it. Prominent researchers Straus and Kantor[5] conclude that human beings have a capacity for violence and if a specific home life situation has a certain amount of baseline violence within it (eg, spanking the children, pushing or slapping between spouses) in addition to the presence of verbal aggression, the environment is more likely to give rise to physical abuse.

CORPORAL PUNISHMENT

The relationship between the use of corporal punishment and the risk of maltreatment remains an area of concern to child health professionals. *Corporal punishment* is a disciplinary method in which physical force is used as a behavioral modifier. Ninety percent of families in the United States report having used spanking as a means of discipline at some time.[6] Corporal punishment has its roots in personal, cultural, religious, and societal views of children and how they are to be disciplined. It can be inflicted through pinching, spanking, paddling, shoving, slapping, shaking, hair pulling, choking, excessive exercise, confinement in closed spaces, and denial of access to a toilet. Approximately half of pediatricians in the United States report being generally opposed to the use of corporal punishment, and about one third are completely opposed to its use.[7] Three fourths of the pediatricians reported having been spanked when they were children.[7]

The American Academy of Pediatrics (AAP) offers guidance for effective discipline that does not involve corporal punishment. Via a review of the existing professional literature, it provides the following reasons why corporal punishment, specifically spanking, does not offer an effective long-term strategy to reduce undesirable behaviors[8]:

— Spanking children younger than 18 months increases the chance of physical injury, and the child is unlikely to understand the connection between the behavior and the punishment.

— Although spanking may result in a reaction of shock by the child and cessation of the undesired behavior, repeated spanking may cause agitated, aggressive behavior that may lead to a physical altercation between parent and child.

— Spanking models aggressive behavior as a solution to conflicts and has been associated with increased aggression in preschool- and school-aged children.

— Spanking and threats of spanking lead to altered parent-child relationships, making discipline substantially more difficult when physical punishment is no longer an option, such as with adolescents.

— Spanking is no more effective as a long-term discipline strategy than other approaches, and reliance on spanking makes other disciplinary strategies less effective. Time-out and positive reinforcement of other behaviors are more difficult to implement and take longer to become effective when spanking has previously been the primary method of discipline.

— Once spanking begins, it can create a pattern that is difficult to escape. Because spanking may provide the parent some relief from anger, the likelihood that the parent will spank the child in the future is increased.

The arguments against corporal punishment are not attempting to imply that caregivers should not discipline their children at all. In fact, discipline is viewed as a necessary component for child rearing. However, problems arise when discipline is not handled appropriately. Examples of appropriate discipline are limit setting, teaching right from wrong, assisting in decision making, and helping the child develop a sense of self-control.[9] No credible evidence exists in medical literature to prove that corporal punishment is more effective than a consistently-applied disciplinary alternative. A comprehensive review of 60 references confirmed this claim.[6]

Parents and caregivers who utilize corporal punishment are often angry, irritable, depressed, fatigued, and stressed. They apply the punishment at a time that they "have lost it" and frequently express remorse and agitation while punishing their children. One concern is that, if initial uses of moderate physical force do not cause the child to stop misbehaving, the caregiver's anger and frustration may increase, thus leading to greater use of physical force. In these scenarios, the potential quickly emerges for the caregiver to lose control and injure the child. Regardless of whether an injury is the intended outcome, it may very well be the result.

Alternatives to Corporal Punishment
As stated above, the disciplinary method preferred by many health care professionals is a consistent, nonphysical approach, including such measures as time-outs, loss of

privileges, expressions of parental disappointment, and grounding. Not only do these measures avoid putting the child at risk, they also model nonviolent behavior.

The AAP offers its insights into using effective discipline strategies that do not rely on physical force. In discussing consistent use of positive techniques, the AAP recommends that the following will make these developmentally appropriate strategies more effective[8]:

— Clarity on the part of the parent and child about what the problem behavior is and what consequence the child can expect when this behavior occurs

— Providing a strong and immediate initial consequence when the targeted behavior first occurs

— Consistently providing an appropriate consequence each subsequent time a targeted problematic behavior occurs

— Delivering instruction and correction calmly and with empathy

— Providing a reason for a consequence for a specific behavior, which helps children beyond toddler age learn the appropriate behavior and improves their overall compliance with requests from adults

The time-out technique is clearly and practically described by author and parent educator Elizabeth Pantley. (For more information on her techniques, visit her Web site at http://www.pantley.com/elizabeth.) Her work is used extensively within the materials distributed by the US Department of Health and Human Services' (USDHHS) Administration for Children and Families as part of its "Gateways to Prevention" packet.[10] This packet was issued to recognize the 20th anniversary of the first presidential proclamation of April as Child Abuse Prevention Month.

Time-outs are viewed as an effective, positive technique for preadolescents. They serve 3 different disciplinary purposes[10]:

1. They give children time and space to cool off, calm down, and reconsider their options to behave or misbehave in a given situation.

2. They give the parent or caregiver time and space to cool off and calm down in order to be able to reestablish control over the situation and model ways of staying in control to the children involved.

3. They provide a specific method to nonviolently stop a specific behavior that still delivers a message that the behavior is not acceptable and must stop immediately.

The following are tips for effective use of the time-out punishment:

— Apply the time-out quickly: It should be issued at the time of the behavior and not as a delayed reaction.

— Use it selectively and consistently around very specific behaviors such as whining, for example, but do not overuse it because it will lose its effectiveness.

— Stay calm and control your emotions while applying it.

— Be committed to using it every time the specific behavior appears.

As mentioned above, time-outs are geared primarily toward preadolescents. For teenagers, who are developmentally more capable of negotiating rules and consequences, Elizabeth Pantley suggests thinking through the consequences that will be imposed for various behaviors in advance and making an effort to manage one's own anger and frustration prior to talking with the teenager.[10] The goals of disciplining a teenager are to prevent unacceptable behavior and teach them how to make responsible decisions. With regard to rules, Pantley suggests periodic reassessment to ensure they are reasonable, understood, enforceable, and consistent. If all goes well, the rules may be relaxed and renegotiated as the teenager becomes more mature. On the other hand, if a teenager is not making mature decisions, it may be necessary to tighten rules or increase parental supervision. All teenagers may be expected to challenge rules, and when this occurs the consequences must follow in a consistent manner.

Discipline is a very real and necessary part of parenting and child rearing. However, it is not limited in meaning to the use of corporal punishment. Enough concerns exist about the long-term effectiveness of corporal punishment to dissuade its use. Ample evidence exists to show that it may, albeit infrequently and unintentionally, lead to situations where the level of physical force becomes angry and uncontrolled, crossing the line into physical abuse by injuring the child. Good, effective discipline begins long before the bad behavior needs to be controlled and is rooted in a well-functioning family that focuses on healthy development and effective parenting and childrearing practices (**Table 2-2**). The AAP's Committee on Psychosocial Aspects of Child and Family Health outlines a set of conditions that a family may want to incorporate into the way it views discipline and parent-child relationships. If consistently held, the following conditions should promote a healthy family environment wherein child behavior can be effectively managed[8]:

— Maintaining a positive emotional tone in the home through play and parental warmth and affection for the child

— Providing attention to the child to increase positive behavior or, conversely, withholding attention to decrease undesirable behaviors; note that, for older children, attention includes being aware of and interested in their school and other activities

— Providing consistency in the form of regular times and patterns for daily activities and interactions; doing so should reduce resistance, convey respect for the child, and make negative experiences less stressful

— Responding consistently to similar behavioral situations to promote more harmonious parent-child relationships and more positive child outcomes

— Being flexible, particularly with older children and adolescents, through listening and negotiation to reduce fewer episodes of child noncompliance with parental expectations

— Involving the child in decision-making to enhance long-term moral judgment

DOMESTIC VIOLENCE

The relationship between domestic violence and child physical abuse is receiving increasing attention. Statistics suggest an overlap between the violence that occurs in a family where one of the caregivers, often the mother, is harmed and the violence that children experience. Between 3.3 and 10 million children each year witness episodes of family violence in their households.[9] Even if the children are not always physically harmed, children whose mothers are victims of domestic violence are 6 to 15 times more likely to be maltreated than are other children.[11] This overlap between domestic violence and child physical abuse was documented in a 1998 federal government report titled *In Harm's Way*, which reviewed important research involving both problems (**Figure 2-2**).

Table 2-2. Dos and Don'ts for Effective Prevention of Misbehavior

Recommendations	Comments
Do make sure your children understand that you are the parent.	You can and should negotiate, explain, and share decision making with your children, but ultimately you may have to set the limits and enforce the rules.
Do recognize your children when they behave well.	Whenever appropriate, praise, reward, and encourage your children for their good behavior.
Don't compare children or hold one up as better than the other.	Avoid saying things like, "Why can't you be as good as your brother? He never gives me any aggravation." Such statements are destructive on multiple fronts.
Do use reasonable reprimands rather than harsh threats.	If you depend mostly on reward and praise, you rarely have to punish children, especially those at the preschool level. With generally well-behaved children, it is often sufficient to merely suggest the threat of some unknown punishment when they misbehave.
Do teach your children to express emotions verbally.	Teaching children to say, "I'm angry that you said that to me," or, "You hurt my feelings," is better than expressing anger through negative behavior.
Do model positive behaviors.	If you want your children to develop wise spending habits, let them see you make budgetary sacrifices and hear your reasoning for doing so.
Don't model negative behaviors.	If your do not want your children to smoke, then you should not smoke.
Do have patience.	If you have a temper problem, deal with your children constructively. Manage your temper, especially when in front of or within earshot of the children. If this does not work, seek help.
Do be affectionate with your children at least once daily.	Frequently tell your children that you love them and are proud of them. Model appropriate public displays of affection with your spouse in front of your children. This includes spontaneous hugs and kisses and verbal expressions of fondness and regard.
Do consistently teach empathy, cooperation, and well-reasoned problem solving.	Convince your children to do the right thing because it is the right thing to do, not because of fear of punishment.
Don't scream at or psychologically "put down" your children.	Emotional maltreatment consists of sarcasm, ridicule, name-calling, putdowns, and scapegoating.
Do implement a consistent parenting plan that is used by all who care for your children.	At an early age, children will recognize that they can play one parent against the other when there are inconsistencies in parenting styles.

(continued)

Table 2-2. *(continued)*

RECOMMENDATIONS	COMMENTS
Do be aware of developmental milestones and age-appropriate expectations.	Recognize the emergence of expected behaviors, including such appropriate ones as walking and talking and such inappropriate ones as temper tantrums and sibling rivalry.
Don't mimic ineffective, trans-generational parenting.	Unless you have taken specific courses in parenting, you are probably disciplining your children similarly to how you were disciplined. Do not unconsciously use the same ineffective phrases and admonitions that infuriated you when your parents repeated them over and over. You probably learned to tune them out so that they had no effect whatsoever, and your children will do the same.
Do be as objective as possible.	Use humor and do not always take yourself seriously. You will make mistakes, but be able to step back and see the humor in them.
Do incorporate rational, moral persuasion to teach your children appropriate behavior.	Although you do not always have to give children reasons for why they should behave in a certain way, do it as much as you can. Of course, you may not always be able to. After repeated discussions of the same topic, you may sometimes have to say, "You must do it because I say so. I am your parent, I love you, and I know best."
Don't let yourself get out of control when disciplining your children.	Walk away first if possible, and then come back when you are rational. Know how you handle stress and disappointment. Learn how to tell if you are getting angry and if you are at risk of losing control.
Do set limits and provide structure.	Make sure that your children know what behaviors are unacceptable, and make sure that you respond consistently when rules are broken. Children should also know how highly you value specific acceptable behaviors.
Don't threaten unreasonable punishment or use threats that you will not carry out.	Your children will learn that they can get away with anything when you have proven you will not actually punish them.
Do make time to watch educational television with your children.	Watch shows with your children that teach moral messages or use stories that leave open the possibility of discussing the moral or immoral behaviors of the characters. After watching, talk about what you have just seen.
Do monitor television viewing, and limit exposure to violent content.	Prevent or limit viewing of programs that present violent solutions to problems.

Adapted from Hyman[7] with permission of John Wiley & Sons, Inc. Copyright © 1997.

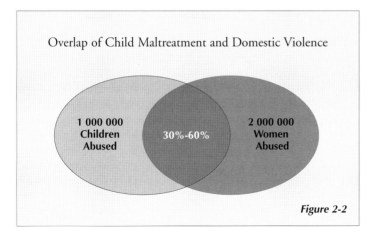

Overlap of Child Maltreatment and Domestic Violence

1 000 000 Children Abused

30%-60%

2 000 000 Women Abused

Figure 2-2

Figure 2-2. There is a 30% to 60% overlap between abused children and abused women in the same family. Reprinted from the National Clearinghouse on Child Abuse and Neglect.[12]

Figure 2-3. Areas where accidental injuries generally occur.

Figure 2-4. Areas where abusive injuries generally occur.

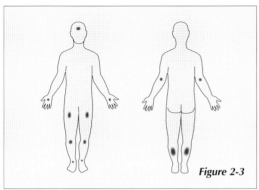

Figure 2-3

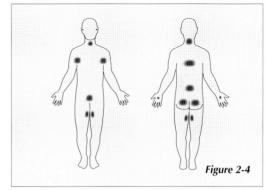

Figure 2-4

INJURIES IN CHILDREN

COMMON ACCIDENTAL INJURIES

Children are curious, typically "on the move," and generally exploring what is in front of them. As a result, many accidental injuries can occur, often to the front of their body and involving the skin's surface. Typical injuries include bruises or cuts on the forehead, nose, chin, palms, elbows, shins, and knees (**Figure 2-3**). Hand injuries—usually on the palm in younger children and the fingertips in older children—can accidentally occur when, for instance, a child breaks a fall or is exploring an object. Minor injuries can also occur on more fleshy areas, such as the thighs and calves, when children accidentally bump into something or during "rough and tumble" play. Accidental falls and bumps usually cause injuries that are not symmetrical because children fall to the left or right or use one hand or the other to explore.

TYPICAL ABUSIVE INJURIES

One way that injuries such as bruises, cuts, burns, and bone fractures can reveal abuse is when they occur in places that are unlikely to have been injured accidentally. Injuries to the buttocks, genital area, abdomen, and back, as well as injuries on the protected sides of the body—particularly the sides of the chest near the armpits and the inner part of the thighs close to the groin—are often signs of abuse (**Figure 2-4**). An accidental bruise on any of these places is highly unusual.

Age can also be a useful indicator when diagnosing an injury. Infants who do not walk rarely develop bruises. Children who are toddling can fall and develop injuries, but they tend to hit against the floor, furniture, or walls in characteristic ways. Injuries to the backs of hands are always suspicious because children do not explore with the backs of their hands. Furthermore, the hands are a common area where caregivers inflict punishment.

The head and face are common areas of both accidental and abusive injury. Approximately half of all physical abuse victims have head or facial injuries. A variety of injuries to the skin, bones, and head and face can be attributed to common household falls, but children usually suffer only minor injuries when they fall accidentally out of bed, from a sofa, off a chair, or down the stairs. When an object such as a tricycle or stroller is involved, injuries can be more severe. Occasionally, in routine falls, children may suffer a single skull fracture. Complex injuries and severe brain injuries are very uncommon and result from significant, and typically abusive, falls. If the child suffers an injury to the ears, cheeks, temple, or tongue—all areas that would not be injured with falls forward—physical abuse needs to be considered. Cuts, bleeding, swelling, and redness of the ear and the soft tissues lining the outer ear canal may be evidence of a severe blow to the ear.

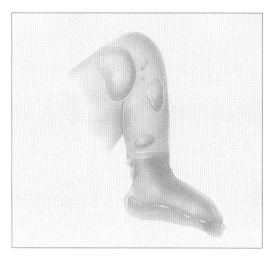

Figure 2-5. *Stocking-glove immer-sion burn of the foot. The sole is spared because it was in contact with the bottom of the bathtub. There are also splash burns on the upper leg.*

Burns that raise the suspicion for abuse are scalds, which occur when children are exposed to a hot liquid (usually hot water or grease), or contact burns resulting from contact with a hot surface, such as an iron or a cigarette. As with other types of abusive injuries, abusive burns may appear in unusual locations, such as on the buttocks and genital area. They may also be in a shape that is unlikely to have occurred naturally, such as the "stocking-glove" pattern (**Figure 2-5**), wherein there is a sharp line between burned and unburned skin instead of the ragged edge that would result from a splash. If a hand or foot is plunged into a hot liquid, it may produce a forced immersion burn pattern, which is highly suggestive of abuse.

The degree of diaper rashes on an infant can also be a clue to the level of a caregiver's attentiveness. Not all diaper rashes suggest neglect—the skin of some infants is more sensitive than others, and some irritation and redness will normally occur. It is when symptoms are severe, including the presence of peeling, cracked, or bleeding skin, that neglect may be a possibility. Similarly, an infant with a constantly dirty genital area who is left in wet diapers long enough for ammonia burns to occur is not being cared for adequately. These are examples of how neglectful caregiving can lead to abusive injuries.

Bite wounds can be another indicator of neglect. If a child has multiple cat or dog bites and scratches, or multiple bites from other children, when he or she returns from daycare, it may indicate that the child is being left unattended for long periods of time.

Among the most serious injuries that crying infants may be exposed to is shaken baby syndrome (SBS), which is responsible for at least 50% of childhood deaths resulting from nonaccidental trauma.[13] It causes the most severe, permanent effects and disability of all mechanisms of abuse. With shaking, children suffer a whiplash injury to the brain similar to that which results from a car crash. The skull and brain move in different directions during the shaking as the head rotates on the neck, stretching and tearing the blood vessels, and injuring the brain directly as well. Shaking tends to occur when a frustrated caregiver loses control when dealing with a crying infant.

Another sign of abuse is when multiple injuries are present during various stages of healing. Such a pattern indicates intentional abuse since it cannot be explained by a single incident. **Table 2-3** summarizes some of the more detailed information related to SBS and other abusive injuries.

ASSESSING CAREGIVER HISTORY OF INJURIES

When an injury looks suggestive of abuse, the first question to ask is, "Could this injury have occurred in the way the caregiver described?" Any significant discrepancy between the physical findings and the offered explanation is a sign of possible physical abuse. Three types of discrepancies include:

Table 2-3. Details Surrounding Abusive Injuries

INJURY	DETAILS
Bruises	Bruises are caused by the collection of blood under the skin and will be visible for days to weeks. They change color over time and typically progress from red and blue to various shades of green, yellow, and brown before totally fading. Bruises that may indicate physical abuse appear: — In multiples and at different stages of healing. — In unexpected locations, including such protected areas as the neck, armpit, or inner thigh. — In the shape of an object, such as folded cords, belt buckles, or handprints. (Bruises in this category are referred to as "patterned injuries.")
Burns	Abusive burning occurs most often in younger children and during times of peak stress in the caregiver's day. Some may be associated with the frustration that arises when the child has a wetting or soiling "accident" during toilet training. The following water temperatures and exposure times will cause a second-degree burn: — 125° F (52.8° C); 2 minutes. — 130° F (55.6° C); 30 seconds. — 140° F (61.1° C), the average high temperature for most households; 5 seconds — 158° F (71.1° C); less than 1 second Hot objects, such as vents, curling irons, and steam irons, may cause patterned burns, which are often indicators of abuse.
Bone fractures	Some breaks are more often associated with physical abuse than others. A leg fracture in an infant who does not yet walk should arouse suspicion. A "corner fracture" at the edge of a bone is also suspicious, as such injuries are typically caused by a forceful tug on an arm or leg. Some bones are commonly fractured accidentally, such as the collar bone (clavicle) and the forearm, while others, such as the ribs, breastbone (sternum), and shoulder blade (scapula) are rarely fractured under typical circumstances.

(continued)

Table 2-3. *(continued)*	

INJURY	DETAILS
Mouth and eye injuries	Lip injuries can involve bruises, cuts, scrapes, or burns. Lip tears can occur after a direct blow to the mouth, with the tear appearing as a ragged line. Bruises, broken teeth, and facial fractures may also be abusive injuries caused by a direct blow. Such injuries may be more common around feeding time, as the frustrated caregiver jams a spoon or bottle into the infant's mouth, ripping the lips and/or damaging other structures.
	It is difficult to break the tissues around the eye and produce a black eye without damaging the nose as well, unless the black eye is caused by a direct blow, such as from a fist. A black eye can also result from a child falling on the center of his or her face, but unless the fall is severe enough to break the nose, it is unlikely that both eyes will be damaged.
Skull and brain injuries	Skull fractures can occur from accidental or abusive falls. Some brain injuries, such as contusions, are directly to the brain. These are bruises resulting from the brain hitting up against the bony skull in which it is housed. Another example of injury directly to the brain is when the blood vessels that make up the blood supply are injured and bleed, affecting the underlying or surrounding area.
Injuries from SBS	Children younger than 2 years can suffer significant brain injury from severe shaking for the following reasons: — The head is quite large in comparison to the body. — The neck muscles are generally weak. — Infants have poor control of their head and neck. — The infant brain has a greater water content than the adult brain. — The infant brain is not as well protected as the adult brain. — The skull is relatively unstable, with the various skull bones not yet firmly attached to one another. Signs of SBS are: — *Altered level of consciousness.* The child may be sleepy, yet irritable, may have seizures, or even be in a coma. Often the child will hold himself or herself stiffly in an unusual posture, suffer respiratory arrest, or die. — *Shock.* The child may be pale, sweating, vomiting, listless, or have difficulty breathing. — *Other injuries.* The child may have abdominal and/or chest injuries.

Data from Monteleone.[14]

— The injury is too severe to have resulted from the described incident or could not have been caused by the incident at all.

— The explanation involves the child doing something that he or she is not developmentally able to do.

— The explanations change over time.

A child's age is crucial in evaluating physical injuries. Infants who cannot yet walk and are receiving good care are rarely injured at all. Infants learning to walk or crawl, however, often fall and suffer single bruises. Accidental injuries require specific motor skills on the part of the child. If a parent or caregiver says an injury was caused by something the child could not physically do, abuse is very likely. Following are examples of motor skills that develop at certain ages:

— With some exceptions, children begin to roll over at the age of 4 months.

— Children begin to crawl at the age of 8 to 10 months.

— Children begin to walk unassisted at about the age of 1 year.

— Children develop the ability to pedal a tricycle at about the age of 3 years.

— Children can comfortably climb steps using alternating feet at about the age of 3 years.

Based on these facts, it becomes obvious that a 2-month-old infant is unable to crawl over to a radiator and get burned, and a 15-month-old child who has suffered a severe burn to the buttock is unlikely to have ridden a tricycle into a space heater. If a caregiver provides an explanation that is as unrealistic as those, he or she may be trying to conceal an act of physical abuse.

Common sense and a sound knowledge of what happens when there are routine accidents in the home can also detect many false explanations. For example, a 17-month-old girl's burned buttocks cannot be plausibly explained by a story describing her climbing onto a space heater and sitting on the top if she lacks burns on her hands and legs. If scrapes and bruises are attributed to a major bicycle accident, they should probably be accompanied by a broken bone. If a caregiver attributes an injury to a second child, consider the ages of the children involved; children can indeed play roughly with each other, but it is highly unlikely that toddlers are developmentally mature enough to injure one another severely.

Finally, explanations for injuries should not change over time. If the history of the injury differs upon retellings, it may be fabricated. Caregivers will often try to invent scenarios that better explain injuries when someone states that their original history fails to adequately explain the child's injury.

HEALTH CARE EVALUATION

When a child is injured, a doctor or a nurse practitioner must perform a complete medical evaluation (**Table 2-4**). Medical histories include the details of when the injury was discovered, who was present at the time, where the child was, and what else was happening around the child. Additionally, the past medical details related to general health, previous trauma and hospitalizations, information as to where the child previously received health care, and the developmental details and social aspects of the child's life need to be recorded. Since physical abuse is often an ongoing pattern of unsafe care, performing a thorough, "head-to-toe" physical examination is essential to finding other areas of either current or previous injury. The order of the physical examination is determined by the condition of the child. Children with less severe injuries who are in a stable condition can have the injured area examined last, since that area is most likely to be uncomfortable.

For accidental injuries, a doctor or nurse practitioner typically expects the clinical history surrounding the injury's discovery and the physical examination to be consistent. History and the physical findings will determine which laboratory and radiological studies are necessary. For children younger than 2 years who are suspected of having been abused physically, a complete set of bone X-rays, called a skeletal survey, is recommended to rule out skeletal injury.

The process of working through the various possible causes should be carefully followed in cases in which abusive injury is a real possibility. This way, the diagnosis of physical abuse can be made confidently and the caregivers will not be inappropriately accused of abuse.

EVALUATION STEPS	DESCRIPTION OF EVALUATION
Table 2-4. Health Care Evaluation for Suspected Physical Abuse	
History	The following basic questions should be asked of the caregiver and, if the child is old enough, of the child as well: — What was the date and time of the injury, and when was it first noted? — Where did the injury occur? — Who witnessed the injury? — What was happening prior to the injury? — What did the child do after the injury? — What did the caregiver do after the injury? — How long after the injury did the caregiver wait before seeking care for the child?
Physical examination	Severely injured children in critical condition first require life-saving measures, then other components of the examination can follow. Physical indicators that should raise the suspicion of physical abuse include: — Injury patterns inconsistent with the history provided. — Multiple injuries or types of injuries. — Injuries at various stages of healing. — Poor hygiene. — The presence of classic physical abuse injuries, including loop marks, forced immersion burns, and symptoms of SBS. Additionally, aspects of the burn physical examination that should raise the concern for possible abuse are: — Burns incompatible with developmental level. — Bilateral or mirror-image burns. — Burns localized to genitals, buttocks, or the surrounding skin (especially at toilet training stage). — Evidence of excessive delay in seeking treatment. — The presence of other forms of injury.
Laboratory studies	If a bleeding problem is suspected, a bleeding evaluation should be done. Toxicology screens may be requested if the clinical situation suggests a possible ingestion. Blood tests for abdominal injury may be requested. Radiology studies such as radiographs (X-rays), computed tomography (CT) scans, and magnetic resonance imaging (MRI) scans may be ordered.

AFTER SUSPECTED PHYSICAL ABUSE IS REPORTED

Child protective services (CPS) agencies in each community are responsible for performing investigations of suspected physical abuse and will rely on the physician and health care team to provide the details of the medical evaluation. CPS will assess the caregivers' background, caregiving abilities and potential, environmental safety, risk for repeat abuse, and risk to other siblings. The assessment will determine the family's treatment plan. A variety of treatment options are available, ranging from periodic contact with the child and family to removing the child from the home temporarily or permanently. The CPS process is fairly standardized, and child maltreatment cases typically involve the following steps[1]:

— *Intake.* Screening of reports and acceptance of the case.

— *Initial risk assessment*. Caregiver interviews, medical information gathering, home evaluation, and the possibility of contact with law enforcement.

— *Case planning*. Determination of the child's safety, with the following 3 options:

— The child goes home with the caregiver, with or without services.

— The child is removed from the home and family with caregivers' consent, and the caregivers are offered services to assist them in working toward reuniting with the child.

— The child is removed from the home and family without caregivers' consent, involving court action and incorporation of legal steps and processes to determine the ultimate plan for the child.

IMPACT OF PHYSICAL ABUSE

Physical abuse is a serious issue and may have physical, psychological, and emotional effects on child victims. Immediate physical consequences vary depending on the type and severity of injury; they are often visible and obvious, and they may have long-term physical consequences. Psychological and developmental effects may be latent and more complex. Children do best when in an environment that provides positive, nurturing interactions that promote developmental and emotional well-being. Anything less can impair a child's development. For example, if the abusive environment interferes with the achievement of an internal sense of safety and trust, children may have difficulty attaining developmental tasks related to cooperation and interactive play. Typical negative impacts of physical abuse and neglect include behavioral difficulties related to self-control such as aggression, violence, and juvenile delinquency; psychosocial and cognitive problems such as decreased school achievement; and psychological disorders such as poor attachment, empathy, and self-esteem. However, the extent of the negative impact on the child's psychological and developmental progress can be lessened by the various mediating factors, which include the child's coping strategies, the child's personality characteristics, supportive people in the child's environment, and perceived level of response to the identification of the abuse and neglect once they come to light. **Table 2-5** lists some of the consequences seen after child abuse and neglect.

From a mental health perspective, physical abuse can have profound effects on the child's emotional and mental well-being. A small number of children will have minimal mental health impairment resulting from abuse, but the majority will experience at least a moderate impact and some will experience severe effects, including posttraumatic stress disorder and dissociative syndromes.

Psychologists and psychiatrists divide the mental impacts of child maltreatment into 3 phases: the immediate impact of the abuse, the impact of ongoing and continual abuse, and the long-term impact on a child's adulthood. In the first phase, initial reactions to the abuse are visible and may include anxiety, stress reactions, alterations in developmental functioning (eg, regressing to an earlier stage), withdrawn affect, aggressive affect, or cognitive distortions. Ongoing abuse produces a type of accommodation to the environment that may include forms of learned helplessness and minimization of the physical and emotional pain being experienced. The third phase involves long-term effects that negatively impact a child's ability to work, achieve, and form meaningful relationships later in life.

At times, people question whether children who are abused are more likely to become abusers than children who are not. The evidence that has amassed over 2 decades of professional study reveals that the majority of children who are abused and neglected do

Table 2-5. Consequences of Physical Abuse	
Health and physical effects	— Immediate: bruises, burns, cuts, broken bones, organ injuries, and bleeding — Long-term: brain damage, scarring, disfigurement, permanent disabilities, and death

Effects on brain development	— Because of the reaction to persistent stress associated with child abuse and neglect:
	  — Brain may develop enhanced pathways for the fear response.
	  — Brain may become "wired" to experience the environment as hostile and uncaring.
	  — Child may have trouble controlling his or her emotions and behaving or interacting appropriately and may demonstrate impulsive behavior, difficulties in social interactions, or a lack of empathy.

Behavioral impacts	— Behaviors range from passive and withdrawn to active and aggressive. They may also include:
	  — Low self-esteem.
	  — Depression and anxiety.
	  — Posttraumatic stress disorder.
	— The following may be seen in adolescents and adult survivors:
	  — Depression
	  — Higher-risk behaviors, such as smoking and alcohol and drug use
	  — Attachment difficulties
	  — Eating disorders
	  — Poor peer relations
	  — Suicide attempts
	  — Difficulty maintaining relationships with peers

Data from Goldman et al.[1]

not grow up to become delinquent, criminal, or violent.[15] Being exposed to a violent environment is certainly a risk factor for the development of adult criminal behavior and an abusive parenting style, but it does not guarantee it. Only one fourth to one third of children exposed to physical abuse later abuse their own children.[1]

CONCLUSION

Physical abuse is damaging to a child's physical, mental, and emotional well-being; to families; and to communities. All adults should be familiar with the warning signs of physical abuse and be prepared to respond. If a child appears to be a victim of physical abuse:

— Ask questions of the caregiver. Try to get a clear idea of how the injury occurred. If possible, talk to more than one person who was present.

— Evaluate whether the injury could have been caused in the way it was described. Does the report make sense? Does it seem to fit with the child's developmental abilities? Do you feel that the situation is adequately explained? Do details of the story change during each retelling?

— Ask the child what happened. Listen to his or her answer and believe any report of abuse or neglect. Children, especially young children, do not generally lie about abuse.

— Take the child to a doctor's office or hospital for a professional evaluation. If you ever have any doubt, seek professional help.

— If you seriously suspect abuse or neglect, report the incident to the child abuse hotline in your area or, if your area does not have a local number, to the national hotline.

REFERENCES

1. Goldman J, Salus MK, Wolcott D, Kennedy KY. *A Coordinated Response to Child Abuse and Neglect: The Foundation for Practice.* Washington, DC: Office on Child Abuse and Neglect, US Dept of Health & Human Services; 2003. Available at: http://www.nccanch.acf.hhs.gov/pubs/usermanuals/foundation/foundation.pdf. Accessed June 30, 2006.

2. Prevent Child Abuse America. *Recognizing Child Abuse: What Parents Should Know.* Chicago, Ill: Prevent Child Abuse America; 2003. Available at: http://www.prevent childabuse.org/publications/parents/downloads/recognizing_abuse.pdf. Accessed July 7, 2006.

3. US Department of Health & Human Services, Administration on Children, Youth and Families. *Child Maltreatment 2004.* Washington, DC: US Government Printing Office, 2006. Available at: http://www.acf.hhs.gov/programs/cb/pubs/cm04/index.htm. Accessed June 30, 2006.

4. Helfer RM. The etiology of child abuse. *Pediatrics.* 1973;51(suppl 4):777-779.

5. Straus MA, Kantor GK. Stress and child abuse. In: Helfer RE, Kempe RS, eds. *The Battered Child.* 4th ed. Chicago, Ill: University of Chicago Press; 1987.

6. McCormick KF. Attitudes of primary care physicians toward corporal punishment. *JAMA.* 1992;267:3161-3165.

7. Hyman IA. *The Case Against Spanking: How to Discipline Your Child Without Hitting.* San Francisco, Calif: Jossey-Bass Publishers; 1997.

8. American Academy of Pediatrics, Committee on Psychosocial Aspects of Child and Family Health. Guidance for effective discipline. *Pediatrics.* 1998;101:723-728. Available at: http://pediatrics.aappublications.org/cgi/content/full/101/4/723. Accessed June 30, 2006.

9. American Academy of Pediatrics Committee on Child Abuse and Neglect. The role of pediatricians in recognizing and intervening on behalf of abused women. *Pediatrics.* 1998;101:1091-1092.

10. US Department of Health & Human Services, Administration for Children and Families. *Gateways to Prevention: What Everyone Can Do to Prevent Child Abuse.* Washington, DC: USDHHS; 2004. Available at: http://nccanch.acf.hhs.gov/topics/prevention/order/packet2004.pdf. Accessed July 7, 2006.

11. Graham-Bermann SA. Child abuse in the context of domestic violence. In: Myers JEB, Berlinger L, Briere J, Hendrix CT, Jenny C, Reid TA, eds. *The APSAC Handbook on Child Maltreatment.* 2nd ed. Thousand Oaks, Calif: Sage Publications; 2002:119-130.

12. National Clearinghouse on Child Abuse and Neglect (NCCAN). *In Harm's Way: Domestic Violence and Child Maltreatment.* Washington, DC: NCCAN; 1998. Available at: http://www.calib.com/dvcps/facts/harmway.doc. Accessed June 30, 2006.

13. Reece RM, Nicholson CE, eds. *Inflicted Childhood Neurotrauma: Proceedings of a Conference Sponsored by Department of Health and Human Services [et al], October 10 and 11, 2002, Bethesda, Maryland.* Elk Grove Village, Ill: American Academy of Pediatrics; 2003.

14. Monteleone JA. Physical indicators of abuse. In: *A Parent's & Teacher's Handbook on Identifying and Preventing Child Abuse.* St. Louis, Mo: GW Medical Publishing; 1998:15-31.

15. Widom CS. Does violence beget violence? A critical examination of the literature. *Psychol Bull.* 1989;106:3-28.

Chapter 3

CHILD SEXUAL ABUSE

Angelo P. Giardino, MD, PhD, MPH, FAAP

Child sexual abuse is a form of maltreatment in which a child's trust of a more powerful person is betrayed for that person's own sexual pleasure. This type of abuse can be difficult to detect, and in fact sometimes goes completely undiscovered, partially because the abusers (also called perpetrators) are often skillful at persuading children not to inform others of the sexual abuse. Identifying and preventing further abuse requires education. Knowledge of the typical progression towards sexual abuse, the perpetrators' characteristics, and common presenting symptoms are the first steps. Informed parents, teachers, and caregivers can all recognize children who are in danger of being sexually abused and support them through the investigation processes that accompany reports of sexual abuse.

DEFINITIONS

Child sexual abuse is defined as the involvement of children in sexual activity by an older or more powerful caregiver. Children are naturally curious and may engage in developmentally normal sexual play with age-mates, as when two 5 year olds play "doctor" and mutually explore each other's bodies, but a 5-year-old child who plays "doctor" with a 15-year-old babysitter or a stepfather is being sexually abused. Even when the persons in question are both minors, if one is older (typically by greater than 5 years difference in age) and has greater power and knowledge that he or she can use against the other child, the activity is considered sexual abuse. If the perpetrator is not a caregiver, the sexual activity is considered *sexual assault.*

Child sexual abuse and sexual assault may occur as part of activities called *sexual exploitation*, namely producing, collecting, and distributing child pornography or involving children in prostitution. These activities are sometimes called commercial sexual exploitation of children (CSEC) when perpetrators engage in the activities for financial gain. Adolescent runaways are at particular risk for some CSEC activities because of the vulnerable circumstances they are in. In discussing definitions of child sexual abuse, there are several levels of definitions that are important to consider. **Table 3-1** provides an overview of some of the different definitions that one might encounter when reading legal and clinical material or articles on child sexual abuse, sexual assault, and CSEC.

Some of the specific activities that are considered sexually abusive include the following:

— An abuser sexually touching and fondling a child

— Having the child touch the abuser's genitals or perform oral sexual acts on the abuser

— The abuser having vaginal or anal sexual intercourse with a child, whether in a forced or unforced manner

— Purposefully showing the child adult sexual activity, pornographic movies, or photos

— Having a child pose, undress, or perform in a sexual manner

— Spying on a child while he or she is undressing in a private setting such as a bathroom or bedroom

Of the activities listed, the noncontact activities can be the hardest to define. Families may be comfortable with nudity in the home—sharing bathrooms, sharing bedrooms, or otherwise living in small quarters where privacy is at a minimum—which is not

Table 3-1. Understanding the Definitions

TYPE OF DEFINITION	DESCRIPTION
Legal, civil: used by child protection professionals to define the condition of child sexual abuse	Child protection laws hold sexual abuse as a condition from which children need to be protected. Thus, these laws include child sexual abuse as one of the forms of maltreatment that must be reported by designated professionals and investigated by child protection agencies. Courts may remove children from their homes in order to protect them from sexual abuse. Generally, child protection statutes apply only to situations in which offenders are the children's caregivers. The federal definition of child maltreatment is included in the Child Abuse Prevention and Treatment Act (CAPTA). Sexual abuse and exploitation is a subcategory of child abuse and neglect.
Legal, criminal: used by police departments and prosecutors	Criminal laws prohibit certain sexual acts and specify the penalties. Generally, these laws include child sexual abuse as one of several sex crimes. Criminal statutes prohibit sex with a child, regardless of the adult's relationship to the child, though incest may be dealt with in a separate statue. Types of sexual abuse are often classified in terms of degree of severity, first degree being the most serious and fourth degree being the least. The penalties vary depending on: — *The age of the child.* Crimes against younger children are regarded as worse. — *The level of force.* The severity of the crime increases with the force used. — *The relationship between victim and offender.* An act against a relative or household member is considered more serious. — *The type of sexual act.* Acts of penetration receive longer sentences.
Professional/clinical: used by clinicians and professionals who work in the child abuse field	Clinical definitions of sexual abuse are guided by legal definitions but are most concerned with the traumatic impact on the child. Three factors shape the traumatic impact: — *Power differential.* Power can derive from the relationship between the child and abuser, the size or capability of the abuser, and the abuser's ability to psychologically manipulate the child. — *Knowledge differential.* This implies that the abuser is either older, more developmentally advanced, or more intelligent than the victim. — *Gratification differential.* Although perpetrators may attempt to arouse their victims, the goal of the encounter is gratification for the perpetrator.

Adapted from Faller.[1]

automatically abusive. Generally, exposure becomes sexual abuse when it is done to arouse the perpetrator.

Three other terms are vital to discussions of child sexual abuse. The first, *intrafamilial abuse*, sometimes referred to as *incest*, is sexual activity between individuals, including steprelatives, who are related or considered family. These individuals are not permitted to marry one another. In the cases involving stepfamily, the presence or absence of blood relationship is not as important as the kinship role the abuser has in relation to the child. The second term, *pedophilia*, is the preference of an adult for sexual contact with children. Pedophiles are typically skilled at connecting with children and are likely to target the most vulnerable and easily manipulated among them for sexual contact. Finally, *rape* is a legal term defined by various statutes, typically seen as a violent act that includes some degree of forced sexual intercourse. Rape includes actual or threatened physical force sufficient to make the victim feel threatened.

Child sexual abuse is a unique form of victimization and differs markedly from adult sexual assault in several important ways (**Table 3-2**). First, sexual abuse of children commonly unfolds over time through a series of abusive activities that may occur over weeks, months, or years. Adult sexual assault, on the other hand, often occurs as a single, violent episode. Perpetrators of child sexual abuse are typically trusted caregivers known to children and their families. Although the perpetrator of adult sexual assault may be a family member (as in cases of domestic violence) or an acquaintance (as in date rape), the perpetrator is more often a stranger not known to the victim. Child sexual abuse is not often physically violent because perpetrators are able to manipulate the child's trust and do not desire to get caught. Adult sexual assault, on the other hand, commonly involves physical violence. These distinctions are not absolute, however, and there is some overlap between what is typically seen as child and adolescent sexual abuse and adult sexual assault.

Table 3-2. Summary of Child Sexual Abuse Versus Adult Sexual Assault

Abuse	Assault
Occurs over time	Often a single event
Usually perpetrated by a trusted caregiver, rarely a stranger	Perpetrator may be either an intimate partner or a stranger
Physical violence uncommon	Physical violence common

SIZE OF THE PROBLEM

Child abuse and neglect is a problem that too many of our children face: about 872 000 children were victims of child abuse in 2004.[2] Of these cases, approximately 10% involved sexual abuse (**Figure 3-1**). The sexual abuse victimization rate is 1.2 per 1000 children, though many researchers consider child abuse statistics to be low estimates since many cases are not reported to authorities. Only recently have professionals started getting better at recognizing cases and encouraging adults and children to report abuse.

CAUSES OF CHILD SEXUAL ABUSE

Although child sexual abuse has no concrete causes, researchers have identified some common patterns in the development and progression of an abusive situation. Early in the professional study of child sexual abuse, Dr. David Finkelhor studied a number of cases of child sexual abuse and identified several similarities among them.[3] He determined a set of 4 "preconditions" that seemed to explain how the situation evolved

Figure 3-1. In 2004, 9.7% of child maltreatment cases involved sexual abuse. Data from USDHHS.[2]

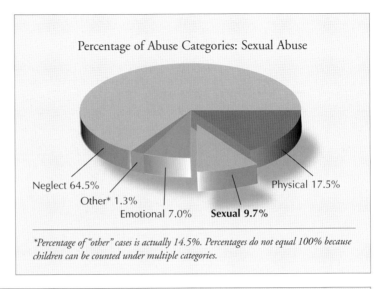

Percentage of Abuse Categories: Sexual Abuse

Neglect 64.5%
Other* 1.3%
Emotional 7.0%   **Sexual 9.7%**   Physical 17.5%

*Percentage of "other" cases is actually 14.5%. Percentages do not equal 100% because children can be counted under multiple categories.

Table 3-3. Finkelhor's 4 Preconditions Explaining how Child Sexual Abuse Occurs

Motivation of the perpetrator	The perpetrator accepts being sexually aroused by children. This acceptance may arise from prior sexual abuse of the perpetrator during childhood, a lack of availability of alternative sources of gratification, or the perpetrator's perception that the alternative sources are less gratifying.
Overcoming internal inhibitions	Although adults may be sexually aroused by children, those obeying their internal codes of behavior and morals typically do not act on these feelings. Sexual abusers, however, overcome their normal internal inhibitions.
Overcoming external inhibitions	The protections that usually exist in a family or caregiving environment such as a school usually prevent child sexual abuse, in that people who are around and looking after the children typically serve as a check against their victimization. Nevertheless, when perpetrators manipulate the situation and are able to isolate the child, typically by taking advantage of the trust that the family or other caregivers have in them, they are able to maltreat the child.
Overcoming a child's resistance	The perpetrator may use direct or implicit coercion to impose age-inappropriate sexual contact upon the psychologically immature child. The abuser manipulates the child and may offer attention in order to ensure participation.

Adapted from Finkelhor.[3]

(**Table 3-3**). Once child sexual abuse begins, a specific progression of events tends to occur. Dr. Suzanne Sgroi and her pioneering colleagues first recognized this pattern and identified a fairly predictable 5-stage sequence that characterized how a lot of cases of child sexual abuse unfold over time.[4] These 5 stages are described in **Table 3-4**.

Table 3-4. Sgroi's 5-Phase Model Explaining a Typical Case of Sexual Abuse	
Engagement	The perpetrator interacts with the child around nonsexual issues and becomes a friend who provides material rewards and meets psychological needs. The perpetrator acquires access to the child and develops a relationship. The child may be sensitive to the threat of losing a relationship that provides attention and perceived affection.
Sexual interaction	The perpetrator involves the child in inappropriate sexual contacts. The sexual contact may progress from exhibitionism and inappropriate kissing to fondling and ultimately to oral-genital, genital-genital, or anal-genital contact. Even if sexual interaction does not progress to fondling and genital contact, the child is still a victim.
Secrecy	Maintaining secrecy, through direct or indirect coercion, is essential to the perpetrator's continued access to the child. The perpetrator may use bribes or threats, which may be as subtle as stating that he or she will disapprove of the child if the child does not comply or as explicit as threatening to harm the child or loved ones.

Disclosure	The disclosure of sexual abuse may occur in either of 2 ways:
	— *Accidental.* There are many different ways for sexual abuse to be accidentally disclosed:
	  — A third party observes the participants and tells someone else.
	  — Signs of physical injury draw outside attention to the sexual behavior.
	  — A sexually transmitted disease or, more rarely, an injury in the genital or anal area is diagnosed.
	  — A pregnancy occurs.
	  — Nonspecific behavior changes are recognized.
	— *Purposeful.* The child consciously reveals the abusive activity. A variety of reasons may exist and vary with the developmental level of the child.

Suppression	Once disclosure takes place, the case may enter a suppression phase. Caregivers may not want to deal with the reality of the disclosure because of denial, fear of family disruption, or guilt. The perpetrator, caregivers, or relatives may exert pressure on the child to retract his or her account of the abusive events. The child's history may be characterized as fabrication or dismissed as fantasy.

Adapted from Sgroi et al.[4]

CHARACTERISTICS OF VICTIMS

Some characteristics make children ideal targets for sexual abusers, including:

— They are naturally curious, even about sex. A clever child molester can exploit this trait to lower a child's inhibitions and seduce the child into sexual activity.

— Children are instructed to respect and obey adults, so adults can easily mislead them.

— Children tend to view adults as being bigger, stronger, and wiser. An adult can use these suppositions to control a child's behavior.

— Children are naturally trusting and can be manipulated by clever abusers to believe that keeping the sexual abuse a "secret" is necessary. Children can be tricked into keeping the inappropriate sexual activity quiet by either direct threats ("I'll hurt you or your parent if you tell") or indirect threats ("If this gets out I'll have to go away, and the family will fall apart because you told").

— Children crave attention, affection, and approval. Children from broken homes and those who are the victims of emotional abuse and neglect are at greatest risk of becoming sexual victims. They can be confused and tricked into thinking that this age-inappropriate sexual activity is a "normal" or acceptable form of attention.

— Adolescents, in their desire for independence, can be trapped into becoming repeat victims. For example, a rebellious adolescent girl who has been victimized fears coming forward, thinking that she will be blamed for the problem because of her disobedience.

CHARACTERISTICS OF ABUSERS

The overwhelming majority of all reported perpetrators of child sexual abuse are male, and they come from a variety of socioeconomic groups, professions, and occupations. Convicted sexual abuse perpetrators are usually known to their child victims. About 30% of all reported perpetrators abused more than one child. In more than half the cases, the victims were younger than 12 years. In general, sex offenders are 7.5 times more likely to be rearrested for a repeat offense than are those convicted of other offenses.[5]

Two broad, overlapping terms are used to describe someone who sexually abuses children: "pedophile" and "child molester." The first term, *pedophile*, refers to an adult who is aroused by and prefers to have sex with children, regardless of whether they actually do. Pedophiles can and sometimes do have sex with adults for a variety of reasons. Sometimes, it is to gain access to children. A pedophile is referred to as such not because of sexual practices, but because of recurrent sexual urges and sexually arousing fantasies involving children. A *child molester*, on the other hand, is an adult who actually does victimize a child. Note that not all child molesters are pedophiles, just as not all pedophiles are child molesters. The difference is that pedophiles experience impulses, whereas child molesters act on them. An example of a person who is a child molester without being a pedophile is someone who prefers to have sex with adults but decides to have sex with a child because of availability or power-related psychological needs.

Psychologists and law enforcement professionals may at times speak of child molesters as being either regressed or fixated. The *regressed* individual has a primary sexual orientation toward adults. However, under conditions of stress or lack of available adult partners, the individual may engage in sex with children. Contrast this with the *fixated* child molester, who does have a primary sexual orientation toward children and would be considered a pedophile acting out fantasies.

IDENTIFYING SEXUAL ABUSE

NONSPECIFIC BEHAVIORAL CHANGES

Symptoms of child sexual abuse can be subtle. The most common indicator is an abrupt change in behavior, often referred to as a *nonspecific behavioral change*. Since physical injury is rarely present, the focus of parents and doctors needs to be on children's disclosure and behavior, not their physical examination. Nonspecific behavioral changes can include both aggressiveness and social withdrawal, even within a single person: Although these 2 behaviors are typically considered opposites, this variation in response arises because children can react to victimization in different ways at different times. Some behaviors are more indicative of abuse than others, but none are a definite sign that abuse has occurred. Nonspecific behavioral changes are not diagnostic of child sexual abuse and may be responses to other difficult situations that occur in the lives of children and families. Divorce, parental job loss, or moving to a new city can all affect a child's behavior.

Often, children do not disclose abuse because they are afraid or confused, or because they may be too young to explain what has happened. When behavioral changes occur, an informed caregiver can respond appropriately. When a child's behavior changes significantly, parents or caregivers should seek appropriate professional guidance and support to help determine what stressful event(s) led to the change. Once the cause has been identified, caregivers can seek out and provide appropriate professional interventions—generally counseling—for the child *and* the family.

A parent or caregiver who is educated and aware of the warning signs of possible child sexual abuse should take steps to immediately intervene on behalf of the child. However, caregivers must be careful not to misinterpret or overinterpret a child's or adolescent's behavior. No matter how aware and informed a caring adult is, it is necessary to understand that the single most important indicator of abuse is a child's *verbal disclosure*. In other words, what the child says has happened is the most concrete evidence that abuse has occurred.

Changes in School Performance

Changes in school performance, grades, and classroom behavior are common among sexually abused children. A child who consistently arrives early to school or leaves school late may be avoiding an unpleasant home situation. However, the child may also be filling a working parent's schedule needs. Rather than assuming that the situation is related to abuse, teachers or other concerned adults should talk with the child to find out what exactly is going on. Parents or caregivers whose life circumstances require them to drop children off early from school and/or pick them up late may want to discuss this situation, or any others that change a child's normal routine, with school personnel so that children are appropriately supervised, cared for, and supported.

Often, caregivers of sexually abused children note a marked decline in children's grades and school performance. The stress of abuse can lead to poor concentration, excessive daydreaming, and a decreased attention span, all of which will interfere with a child's education. Students who once completed all of their homework might start turning it in late or not at all; report cards that used to show A's and B's may now have D's and F's. Of course, abuse is not the only possible cause of declining grades, and so parents and teachers should communicate with one another before jumping to conclusions. The problem may be school related, or the child may simply have a learning disorder, such as dyslexia. The answer could also be a medical problem, like poor vision, which would make seeing the chalkboard difficult and produce a similar drop in grades. Whatever the cause, it is important that the signs do not go unnoticed.

Changes in Peer Relationships

Another sign that abuse may be—but is not necessarily—occurring is when a child's peer relationships change. School-aged children and teenagers may withdraw from social activities. A once-active child might suddenly show little interest in cheerleading, sports, music, or even just "hanging out" with friends. If such changes are observed, they should be a warning that something in a child's life is out of balance, whether it is sexual abuse or something less severe. Whatever the cause, these new behaviors may negatively affect friendships because as they can be taxing on others' patience. Parents can meet with children's teachers and/or school counselor for insight into these situations. Teachers and counselors may be able to help sort through what is going on and provide advice.

Sleep Disturbances

Another possible effect of child sexual abuse is for the victim to experience sleep disturbances; however, there are so many other possible causes of sleep disturbances that abuse should not be seriously considered until those other causes are ruled out. Examples of sleep disturbances include nightmares, night terrors, fear of the dark, refusal to sleep alone, and restlessness.

Change in Appetite

A change in appetite, either an increase or a decrease, is another symptom that abuse sometimes produces in a child. But, once again, abuse is by no means the only explanation. Healthy, nonabused children do exhibit occasional changes in appetite and eating patterns, and these should not be cause for alarm. However, if the appetite change persists, caregivers should take it seriously and look for underlying causes. Even if sexual abuse is not the culprit, there may be another health or social issue that needs attention.

Eating Disorders

Eating disorders are serious problems that require psychological and psychiatric attention. As with the above items, they can be but are not necessarily triggered by sexual abuse. *Anorexia nervosa* is a condition in which an abnormal body image leads a person to self-imposed starvation. *Bulimia* refers to habits of binge eating followed by purging, which is accomplished by self-induced vomiting, laxatives, or diuretics. Any child or adolescent with either of these disorders needs a thorough professional evaluation. Both disorders can be life threatening and seriously alter children's or adolescents' physical health.

Regressive Behavior

Regressive behavior occurs when a child returns to behavior more typical of an earlier developmental stage. For example, a 7 year old who stopped sucking her thumb at 3 years of age and begins sucking her thumb again is regressing. Regressive behaviors are a common coping mechanism among many children and signal that they are under some sort of stress. Other behaviors considered regressive include older children clinging to an adult, talking "baby talk" after learning proper speech, and wetting the bed at night or having bowel and bladder "accidents" during the day after being toilet-trained. Changes in bowel or bladder habits are especially significant signals that something is wrong. Parents may find soiled underwear in closets, under the bed, or in other unexpected places. Before assuming that sexual abuse is the cause, take the child to a doctor for a physical evaluation. Urinary tract infections and gastrointestinal problems also cause bladder or bowel problems, as may less serious types of emotional stress.

Fear

Fear of people, places, or activities not previously feared can be another red flag for sexual abuse. A child might suddenly react hysterically to a visit from a relative or family friend or adamantly refuse to visit a familiar place. It is possible that the relative recently hurt the child physically or sexually, but perhaps the relative was merely strict with the child. Similarly, children refusing to visit a location may have experienced a traumatic event there, or they might have simply fallen down and received a minor bruise. Assess each individual situation carefully and seek out the reasons in a careful and concerned manner. Speak using open-ended questions. Do not ask leading questions, such as whether the relative touched the child inappropriately. Say to the child, "Tell me about your visit with [name of relative]," or, "Draw me a picture about your day at [the place]." Listen to what the child says and give the child the opportunity to tell the story in his or her own words.

Sudden changes in bathtime behavior and/or sudden, unexplained fears of bathing can be particularly significant and should be carefully investigated as well. However, a new reluctance to use a bathroom or shower can also be a reaction to something as simple as being surprised by a spider during a recent visit to the bathroom. Caregivers should seek professional help if children develop fear-related behavior patterns that have no apparently innocent explanation.

Reluctance to Allow Exposure or Examination of Genital Areas

If a child suddenly becomes unwilling to allow someone to bathe him or her or to change a diaper, something may be wrong. However, children sometimes develop genital irritations and resist bathing or cleaning due to an actual physical discomfort. Caregivers should be aware that children, commonly young girls, who take bubble baths or shampoo their hair while sitting in a filled bathtub may develop a genital irritation. If a child shows fear and resistance to genital exposure or cleansing, have a pediatrician evaluate the child for irritations or infections before concluding that sexual abuse is involved.

Sexual Behaviors

Children are naturally curious about their own bodies as well as the bodies of those around them, but their exploration is usually limited to looking and noninvasive touching. The work of Dr. William Friedrich and colleagues, as well as that of other investigators, has illustrated that children's sexual behaviors occur along a continuum that spans from normal to unusual behaviors, the latter of which may be suggestive of sexual abuse[6,7] (**Table 3-5**). Some research suggests increased sexual behaviors may follow from sexual abuse in some children, though other research has clearly demonstrated the presence of widely varied sexual behaviors in a population of nonsexually abused children as well. However, aggressive sexual behaviors, behaviors that imitate adult sexual behaviors, and behavior beyond the usual knowledge of children tend to be relatively rare among those who are not abused. Children exhibiting such behavior should receive prompt medical evaluation.[8]

Sexual acting out, defined as aggressive or adultlike sexual behaviors, may occur between children and their peers, toys, dolls, or stuffed animals. A behavior that is particularly indicative of sexual abuse is a child attempting to sexually victimize another child. In this situation, the child becomes the perpetrator and victimizes other children. This behavior is beyond the limits of the familiar activity of "playing doctor," and it is possible that the child is imitating actions performed on him or her by an adult. Conversely, a victimized child may also be overly friendly to strangers and offer indiscriminate affection—hugging anyone and everyone, climbing onto laps uninvited, holding hands, or even inappropriately touching or kissing someone.

One behavior that parents of sexually abused children find most disturbing is excessive masturbation, described as a child who masturbates frequently with no concern for privacy. A certain amount of masturbation is normal for any child; however, masturbation becomes a problem when it is the primary focus of a child's day and when it is done in the presence of others. When masturbation becomes excessive, sexual abuse

Table 3-5. Normal and Unusual Sexual Behaviors in Children	
STUDY GROUP	SEXUALIZED BEHAVIORS OBSERVED
Among children aged 2 to 12 years old, the 10 *most common* sexualized behaviors were:	— Interest in opposite sex — Trying to look at people undressing — Touching breasts of others (eg, child bumps into teacher and brushes against her breast) — Kissing nonfamily children — Kissing nonfamily adults — Sitting with crotch exposed — Undressing in front of others — Touching sex parts at home — Scratching crotch — Boys and girls playing with toys traditionally associated with the other's gender (eg, boy playing with girl's doll)
Among a similar age group, the 10 *least common* sexualized behaviors were:	— Putting mouth on sex parts — Asking to engage in sex acts — Masturbating with an object — Inserting objects into vagina/anus — Imitating intercourse — Making sexual sounds — French kissing — Undressing other people — Asking to watch explicit television — Initiating sexual behavior with dolls

Data from Hieman et al [8] and Lindblad et al.[9]

is one possible reason, though children who have experienced serious life stresses may also use it as a method to relieve their stress. The comfort, relaxation, and pleasure it produces reinforce the habit. Although excessive masturbation is a potential indicator of sexual abuse, it is not conclusive evidence that abuse has occurred.

Promiscuity

Adolescents who have been sexually abused may become engaged in ***promiscuous sexual behavior***, described as indiscriminate and unrestricted sexual activity with multiple partners. Of particular concern to child health professionals are adolescent girls who were abused as children and may develop destructive dating behaviors, such as:

— Engaging in intercourse at a young age.

— Using drugs and alcohol.

— Having sexual partners who are older and/or more likely to be using drugs and alcohol.

— Failing to use contraception.

— Being involved in a violent dating relationship.

Depression and Suicide Attempts

Children who are depressed may show symptoms of lethargy or social withdrawal. Parents may observe the following characteristics:

— Lack of energy

— Reduced interest in personal hygiene and appearance

— Sad facial expression

— Minimal interaction or play with peers

— Moping

Everyone is sad occasionally and experiences "down days," but children who seem newly or excessively sad or disinterested in their daily routine need medical evaluation.

More overly self-destructive behaviors, such as cutting one's skin or pulling out hair, should prompt immediate referral to a mental health expert. A depressed child who has been severely traumatized by abuse and whose self-esteem has been destroyed is at risk for suicide. Suicidal thoughts, plans, or attempts are severe behavioral indicators. As a caregiver, take any suicidal threat or attempt seriously. Any child of any age who threatens or attempts suicide should have an immediate psychiatric evaluation. Intervene before a suicide threat becomes an attempt.

Delinquency, Substance Abuse, and Running Away

Delinquency involves conflict with the law and committing illegal acts, including property destruction, stealing, and violence. Delinquent behavior may result from many different environmental factors, such as falling in with the "wrong crowd" and giving in to peer pressure to use drugs or turning to drugs as an escape from dealing with being victims of abuse. If delinquency and substance abuse fail to solve children's problems and they cannot cope with the situation, running away from the problem may be a next step. Children or adolescents often incorrectly think that they can find peace by avoiding their problem. Unfortunately, running away puts children in an extremely vulnerable situation that leaves them open to many dangers, one of which is being sexually exploited by people who seek to take advantage of their circumstances.

General Stresses That Cause Behavioral Changes

Stresses not related to child sexual abuse that often create behavioral changes in children include divorce, a parent's remarriage, moving to a new school district, the birth of a sibling, the death of a relative or pet, a parent's loss of employment, and chemical abuse by a member of the family unit. For example, a child whose beloved grandparent has passed away may regress developmentally and start wetting the bed or display unusual anger toward peers or pets. These behaviors are similar to those that occur when a child has been abused. The child may require professional counseling to determine the precipitating stress or to control the resulting behaviors.

Disasters such as 100-year floods, forest fires, domestic and international terrorist attacks, and other catastrophes receiving a lot of media coverage can also distress children. Not only are the events themselves upsetting, but what upsets children even further is to see the effects these events have on adults. Children are exposed to reactions of fear, panic, and desperate sadness, both for individuals and society, and they are not immune to these stressors. The events of September 11, 2001, are a vivid example of how world events can have a direct impact on both adults and children via the massive media coverage that is now possible and easily accessible. In the United

States, nearly every television channel carried coverage of the World Trade Center's collapse. In the aftermath, many children experienced stress-related symptoms, such as nightmares, or regressed to an earlier developmental stage in some way, such as insisting on the use of a night-light that they had long-since abandoned. Children experiencing stress of any magnitude, including events they see on television, may respond by developing behavioral changes. The American Red Cross (http://www.redcross.org) and the American Academy of Pediatrics (http://www.aap.org) each offer materials on their Web sites to help caregivers deal with the stress of such external events that may be traumatic to the children in their care.

PHYSICAL COMPLAINTS

Sexual abuse can cause children to have physical complaints. Perhaps the most obvious examples of these are frequent headaches or abdominal pain ("stomachaches"). Often, no physical cause can be identified, but the symptoms are real, causing a certain amount of distress, and may result in frequent absences from school. When dealing with physical complaints, caregivers should first have children thoroughly examined by their primary health care provider to rule out physical disorders. Also, regardless of the cause of the physical complaints, symptomatic treatment, perhaps with medication or changes in activity, may be necessary to relieve children from pain or discomfort.

Dr. Carol Berkowitz summarized the commonly recognized medical consequences of child sexual abuse. In addition to the immediate injuries and possible sexually transmitted diseases (STDs), the possible physical effects are as follows[10]:

— *Gastrointestinal (GI or "belly-related") disorders.* GI symptoms may commonly be associated with stressful events. Disorders associated with sexual abuse tend to show no structural, infectious, or metabolic basis and as such are called "functional." This does not mean that the symptoms are not real, but rather that obvious tissue injury is not present.

— *Gynecological disorders.* These are related to the inappropriate focus on the child's genital region that may occur in the context of sexual abuse. In general, children with long-term gynecological symptoms associated with child sexual abuse tend to have no specific tissue injury identified, and conditions can include chronic pelvic pain and menstrual irregularities. The common or expected genital symptoms that might be seen in child sexual abuse cases are detailed in **Table 3-6**, along with the various nonsexual-abuse–related medical diagnoses that a primary care physician would consider during a medical evaluation.

— *Varied physical ailments and complaints (technically referred to as "somatization").* These are considered associated with a preoccupation with bodily processes and physical symptoms. Conflicting research in this area makes definitive statements difficult, but some clinical population studies suggest that somatization may account for the reported increase in complaints of chronic headache and backache as well as other vague neurological complaints in children and adults who report having been sexually abused.

HOW TO RESPOND TO SUSPECTED CHILD SEXUAL ABUSE

What should parents and caregivers do if their child comes home from daycare one day with blood in his or her underwear? What if their child suddenly starts behaving differently and refuses to go visit a family friend or relative? What if a child actually says that an adult has touched him or her sexually?

Table 3-6. Genital Symptoms Potentially Seen in Child Sexual Abuse Cases, Along With Possible Other Diagnoses

SYMPTOM/ FINDING	DESCRIPTION	POTENTIAL MEDICAL DIAGNOSES
Genital bleeding	Identification of the source of the blood is necessary to rule out serious injury. Blood-tinged vaginal or urethral discharge initially may be confused for frank bleeding.	— Injury, either accidental or abusive — Foreign body (objects in the vagina) — Local irritation — Skin disorders — Infections, including STDs — Hormonal causes — Cancer-related conditions — Structural abnormalities such as abnormal collection of small blood vessels just under the skin
Vaginal discharge	Normal, clear-white, mucus-like discharge should be differentiated from abnormal discharges related to disease.	— Irritation from either abusive sexual contact, foreign bodies, chemical irritants, or restrictive clothing — Infections, including STDs — Structural abnormalities that cause urine, bowel contents, or infections to drain to the surface
Genital and anal area bruising	Bruising in the genital and surrounding anal area most often represents some type of injury.	— Injury including straddle injury, such as falling against a bicycle's cross bar, or abusive injury — Skin conditions — General body bruising seen in serious blood disorders
Genital and anal area redness	This finding typically represents the result of inflammation.	— Irritation from sexual contact, poor hygiene, restrictive clothing, and chemical irritants — Skin conditions — Infections such as STDs, pinworm, scabies, yeast, or warts — General skin redness seen in some serious diseases that affect the skin

In any of these events, it is important to remain calm and work the situation out in a supportive, constructive manner. Be aware of the child's developmental level, verbal skills, and experience. Young children think in concrete terms and may have limited concepts of numbers and times. Generally, their experiences in life are limited, and their vocabulary will reflect this. For example, if a child says, "he peed in my mouth" or "he got pee on me," the child may not be talking about urine, but rather ejaculated semen. Because children only know one function for the penis, they would likely describe anything that comes out of it as urine. A young girl may say that "he cut me down there with a knife," though there is no evidence of a cut. However, she knows how it feels to be cut with a knife and that was how it felt, so whatever it was that hurt her—a finger, a fingernail, or a penis—was a knife to her.

Do not pressure children for answers. Doing so will make children feel threatened, as if they did something wrong, and they may give false answers because they feel scared. Also, perpetrators sometimes threaten to harm children or their families if children tell anyone about the abuse, and therefore a child may feel in a bind to deny that the abuse occurred in order to protect the threatened loved one. Therefore, maintain a calm, matter-of-fact tone and ask questions in an unthreatening manner. Avoid asking questions that lead children to provide answers they think parents would want to hear. Instead, try to ask open-ended questions that allow children to voice the details they need to bring forward. **Table 3-7** lists some ways to avoid asking leading questions and provides other things to keep in mind while holding these discussions.

HEALTH CARE EVALUATION

Sexually abused children and adolescents must not experience the medical evaluation as another instance in which powerful adults impose authority on their body and remove

---

Table 3-7. How to Productively Discuss Suspected Abuse With Children

ISSUE	CHILD-RELATED PERSPECTIVE
Details	When children remember and talk about a situation, they often concentrate on the central activity and have a very limited recollection of the surrounding details. For example, suppose a 5-year-old girl says that she climbed on an air conditioner and saw the neighboring father sexually abusing his child. When asked where this happened, she says it was in the bedroom. In reality, the air conditioner perch overlooked the kitchen, not the bedroom, so it may be concluded that she was lying. However, it is possible that she was telling the truth. What may have happened is that she correctly remembered the main actions that were taking place (the central information), but the surrounding details of the situation escaped her attention and her memory. There is also the factor that, as more time passes after an event, more details are lost. Even adults miss such peripheral details, especially after a passage of time.
Dates or times	Children can have difficulty with dates and number concepts, such as how many times something happened. A child may easily count to 10, but may not be able to count specific objects. Days of the week and months may not be relevant to a child, but holidays and whether it was cold or hot outside might be easier to keep track of.
Telling the truth	Children may at times lie, as any parent or teacher can readily attest. Usually they do this to get out of trouble or to avoid trouble. They may lie to protect, to deny, or to minimize what happened, or they may withhold information. In general, it tends to be more likely that a child will lie to *deny* that abuse took place than admit it. Also, if he or she is asked repeatedly about it, the child may get tired of telling the same story over and over and embellish the facts to convince or please the questioning adults so that they will stop. Thus, constantly asking the child to recount and relive the situation is not recommended.
Describing people	Be aware that giving a description of a perpetrator is more difficult for a child, especially if the person is unfamiliar. This difficulty is related to the child's focus on the central information rather than on peripheral information or details.

Adapted from Monteleone.[11]

their control of it. If not conducted in a knowledgeable and sensitive manner, the process of taking a complete history, performing a thorough physical examination, and obtaining necessary laboratory tests can be invasive and threatening, serving to further scar the victim. Specially-trained health care professionals working on teams composed of caring doctors, nurses, and social workers should collaborate to optimize this experience for children or adolescents by conveying a gentle, concerned manner and explaining to them what they can expect during the evaluation. A gentle and unhurried approach will help make the health care evaluation part of the recovery process rather than another form of assault and increase the chances of successfully completing the entire evaluation.

The standard health care evaluation of suspected child sexual abuse includes a medical history, physical examination, laboratory assessment, and observations of the caregiver and child (**Table 3-8**). Despite popular belief, most physical examinations of children suspected of having been sexually abused do not yield definitive findings of sexual abuse. The following reasons could account for this:

— The child and family typically know the perpetrator, in which case the use of physical force during the abuse is not as common as it is with adult sexual assaults.

— Disclosure of the abuse is frequently delayed, causing evaluations to be performed weeks to months after the abusive contact when symptoms are much harder to detect, if they are still present at all.

— Even if visible damage was inflicted and the investigation was held soon after the abuse, membranes that compose the genital structures heal rapidly and, often, without obvious scarring.

Table 3-8. Components of the Health Care Evaluation for Suspected Child Sexual Abuse

History/ Interview	Performing a medical history might require an extended period of time in order to help the child feel comfortable and not threatened. The interviewer will use developmentally appropriate questioning and focus on using open-ended, nonleading questions. Interviewers typically speak first with the caregiver alone and then with the child alone. To establish rapport and make the child comfortable, interviews will start with questions such as the following[12]: — Where do you live? Who lives with you? Who visits you? — What school do you go to? What is your favorite subject? — What makes you happy? Sad? Scared? — What kinds of things do you like to do alone? After the child is comfortable, the interviewer will attempt to obtain details of the event with questions like the following[27]: — Are you hurt or sick now? — What happened to you? Where were you? What were you wearing? — What happened next? What else do you remember? — Who did this to you? How do you know this person? — How did this happen? Were you touched with something? Where were you touched? — When did this happen? — Did anyone else see this happen?

(continued)

Table 3-8. *(continued)*	
Physical Examination	To keep the child engaged and calm, the examiner may talk to the child and explain what to expect. Additionally, proper attention to modesty is necessary, and the use of a quiet room with adequate privacy and gowns and drapes is essential.
	The physical examination involves a complete "head-to-toe" examination, in order to avoid reinforcing the focus on the child's genital area that the perpetrator demonstrated during the abuse. With an adult support person of the child's choosing in the room, and an appropriate explanation, the child's genital and anal areas are examined. Prior to puberty, the child's examination will be external only and involve the doctor or nurse practitioner first looking at the external genital and anal structures and then carefully moving the structures to allow for careful inspection of the delicate tissues. The child may be asked to lie on the table in several different examination positions to allow for the most ideal visualization of the genital and anal areas. Some medical centers have a colposcope, which allows for magnification, adequate lighting, and photographic documentation of the examination. Cotton-like swabs may be used to collect samples of secretions and other suspicious materials if deemed appropriate.
Laboratory Studies	Laboratory studies will be conducted to determine if any STDs were passed from the abuser to the child and if there is any evidence left on the child from the abuser.

The health care evaluation leads the physician to a list of possible diagnostic options (called a "differential diagnosis") and, ultimately, to a diagnosis of the item on the list that is most likely to have occurred. The doctors, nurses, and social workers will focus on the health care and well-being of the child and family while documenting and relaying any information obtained during the medical history that will help the investigators and law enforcement prosecute the case. The investigators, on the other hand, explore allegations of suspected maltreatment. Police use findings from the medical evaluation to determine whether a crime has been committed and what appropriate legal action to take. Child protective service (CPS) agencies and workers operate alongside the police to protect children, focusing on each families' ability to function and protect its children. CPS agencies provide support services to families in need and may ultimately remove children from environments determined to be unsafe or unhealthy.

Medical treatment for sexually maltreated children is guided by whatever conditions are uncovered during the health care evaluation and, of course, follow routine standards of care. If a provider diagnoses an STD, it will be treated with appropriate medications based on the child's age and weight. Teenaged girls will be tested for pregnancy. Most importantly, health care providers will be attentive and offer emotional support for the psychosocial crisis in which the child and family now find themselves.

IMPACT OF SEXUAL ABUSE

There is no recognized set of universal responses to or impacts from child or adolescent sexual abuse.[13,14] An individual's response to the trauma of abusive events during childhood differs according to the nature of the abusive experience and the individual's psychological adaptation.[15] The impacts of sexual abuse can be both mental and physical.

The core determinant of the mental health impact is the fundamental harm inflicted upon children by the nonconsensual, inappropriate sexual behavior.[16] A child's self-worth, development, and ability to adjust are all placed at risk by the perpetrator's actions. In evaluating the likely mental health impact on the child, consider the following 3 dimensions of their symptoms:

1. *Severity.* This refers to how strongly children react. Their response to the abuse can range from mild to severe.

2. *Time.* This refers to how elongated children's response is. Do they appear to have healed after a relatively short time period, or are the effects more long-term? In some cases, the effects may even last a lifetime.

3. *Internalization versus externalization.* This refers to the outlet children use to channel their stress. Do they internalize their feelings, becoming withdrawn and depressed, or do they externalize their feelings, becoming aggressive and disruptive?

Keeping in mind that each child has a unique set of coping behaviors and environmental realities affecting the severity, acuity, and expression of his or her response to the sexual abuse, the following are the more common mental health impacts that have been identified[16]:

— *Behavioral problems.* Significant increases in behavioral problems have been observed in children who have been abused, including both generic behavioral problems and increased sexual behaviors.

— *Posttraumatic stress disorder (PTSD) symptoms.* PTSD is related to a child's response to the anxiety surrounding the sexual abuse. Although many children do not meet the full criteria for a formal PTSD diagnosis, many demonstrate several of the symptoms characteristically associated with it.

— *Interpersonal difficulties.* The way children view themselves after abuse occurs will often affect their ability to establish trusting relationships.

— *Cognitive and emotional distortions.* Conflicting evidence exists on this topic, making it difficult to form clear statements, but many child health care professionals agree that abusive experiences are generally associated with various school-related problems, difficult peer relationships, and problematic emotional issues. School performance and emotional functioning appear to be at particular risk.

PTSD and its relationship to sexual abuse have received considerable professional attention. The diagnosis of PTSD in the context of sexual abuse requires the existence of child sexual abuse along with at least one of the following symptoms:

— Frequent reexperiences of the event via intrusive thoughts and/or nightmares

— Avoidance behavior and a sense of numbness toward common events

— Increased arousal symptoms, such as jumpiness, sleep disturbance, and/or poor concentration

Note that since no universal short- or long-term impact of sexual abuse has been identified, neither the presence nor absence of various symptoms or conditions can indicate or disprove sexual abuse.

Individuals considered ***adult survivors of childhood sexual abuse*** are those adults who experience emotional and psychological problems that are attributed to the early damaging effects of the abuse.[17] Some researchers have described a link between sexual abuse and a host of emotional and behavioral dysfunctions. Among these dysfunctions are depression, low self-esteem, suicide attempts, multiple personality disorder, school failure, regressive behavior, PTSD, drug and alcohol abuse, running away, sexual promiscuity, prostitution, and delinquent behavior.[18-20] Dr. Kathleen Kendall-Tackett and her colleagues reviewed 45 studies demonstrating that sexually abused children had more major and minor symptom complaints than did nonabused children.[13] Another group of doctors reviewed 37 published studies on the effects of child sexual abuse, among which there were no uniform long-term consequences, as each case had complex interactions of circumstances.[14] However, most studies of abused children do report that victims experience more depressive symptoms, behavioral problems, and emotional disturbances, even into adult life, than do nonvictims. Additionally, a growing body of literature suggests that child sexual abuse victims may experience higher rates of various physical disorders as adults. Specifically, during the 1980s and early 1990s, public health studies made it clear that risk factors such as smoking, alcohol abuse, and sexual behaviors were not randomly distributed in the population. In fact, a set of studies called the Adverse Childhood Experiences (ACE) studies[21] found that those adults who experienced negative events as children, including family violence and sexual abuse, had more diseases in adulthood.

PSYCHOLOGICAL MODELS

Scientific models help organize information on the possible impact of sexual abuse on children and help make sense of the emotional and psychological effects they experience. No standard or uniform set of responses has yet been identified. Children respond differently to traumatic events, and psychological models illustrate the reasons for these various responses.

CHILD SEXUAL ABUSE ACCOMMODATION SYNDROME

Based on Dr. Roland Summit's clinical experience, child sexual abuse accommodation syndrome is said to have the following 5 stages[22,23]:

1. *Secrecy.* After being abused, a child may be forced to keep the inappropriate sexual contact a secret.

2. *Helplessness.* The victimized child's first reaction to the situation is often to feel trapped and helpless.

3. *Entrapment/accommodation.* As the abusive behaviors persist and the child is coerced into the sexual contact, a feeling of entrapment develops, accompanied by accommodative behaviors. This accommodation is produced because the child fears that no one will believe the story if he or she does tell. Accommodating children are usually part of an environment that has already failed to protect them.

4. *Disclosure.* The victimized child informs others about the abuse that has occurred or is occurring. Not all children perform this stage.

5. *Retraction.* If the child does disclose the abuse but fails to receive adequate support and protection from the people around him or her, the feelings of helplessness are reinforced and may lead the child to retract the disclosure.

TRAUMAGENIC DYNAMICS MODEL

Drs. David Finkelhor and Angela Browne developed a model explaining the psychological injury inflicted on a child who is sexually abused.[24] They proposed a psychological, trauma-oriented model of sexual abuse labeled "traumagenic," an adjective used to describe how certain dynamics come together to cause mental and emotional harm to sexually maltreated children. The framework in this model is based on 4 traumagenic dynamics that are at the core of the injury: traumatic sexualization, betrayal, stigmatization, and powerlessness. These experiences interact to alter the child's cognitive and emotional orientation to the world and distort his or her self-concept, worldview, and capacity to give and receive affection.

CUSTODY ISSUES

Once a sexual abuse allegation is filed, CPS assesses how safe it is for a child to remain at home. Allegations of sexual abuse made during ongoing custody disputes present a particular challenge.[25] Common questions are, "Did the child actually sustain these injuries or did the other parent prompt the child to make the accusations?" and, "Did the parent overreact to a situation that might have been thought of as innocent if there were no custody battle?" The American Bar Association reports that few divorces involve custody disputes and very few involve allegations of sexual abuse.[26] However, Dr. Jan Paradise and colleagues found that in the cases that do involve custody disputes, allegations of sexual abuse were substantiated 67% of the time.[27] Despite professional cynicism, this and other studies have shown that these cases warrant the same comprehensive evaluation as other allegations of sexual abuse and should not be dismissed.

CONCLUSION

The intent of this chapter has been to educate and inform parents and caregivers about the risk of child sexual abuse, not to cause panic about each behavioral change children undergo. Remember, no behavioral indicator is clear evidence that a child has been sexually abused. It is important to be cautious and avoid assuming that abuse must be the answer. Instead, consider these behaviors as warning signs that a child has probably experienced some stressful or traumatic event and is attempting to cope with it. To help the child, take the following steps:

— Remain calm.

— Respond immediately.

— Talk to the child and others who may be involved and have necessary information.

— Take the child for a health care evaluation and, if child sexual abuse is suspected, make sure that appropriate reporting occurs so that a proper investigation may ensue.

— Seek professional counseling for the child and family.

REFERENCES

1. Faller KC. *Child Sexual Abuse: Intervention and Treatment Issues*. Washington, DC: US Dept of Health & Human Services; 1993.Available at: http://nccanch. acf.hhs.gov/pubs/usermanuals/ sexabuse/sexabuseb.cfm. Accessed March 31, 2006.

2. US Dept of Health & Human Services, Administration on Children, Youth and Families. *Child Maltreatment 2003*. Washington, DC: US Government Printing Office, 2005.

3. Finkelhor, D. *Child Sexual Abuse: New Theory and Research*. New York, NY: Free Press; 1984.

4. Sgroi SM, Blick LC, Porter FS. A conceptual framework for child sexual abuse. In: Sgroi SM, ed. *Handbook of Clinical Intervention in Child Sexual Abuse*. New York, NY: The Free Press; 1982:9-37.

5. Sexual abuse statistics. Prevent Abuse Now, PANdora's Box Web site. Available at: http://www.prevent-abuse-now.com/stats.htm. Accessed August 2, 2006.

6. Friedrich WN, Grambsch P, Broughton D, Kuiper J, Beilke RL. Normative sexual behavior in children. *Pediatrics*. 1991;88:456-464.

7. Friedrich WN. Sexual victimization and sexual behavior in children: a review of recent literature. *Child Abuse Negl*. 1993;17:59-66.

8. Heiman ML, Leiblum S, Cohen Esquilin C, Melendez Pallitto L. A comparative study of beliefs about "normal" childhood sexual behaviors. *Child Abuse Negl*. 1998;22:289-304.

9. Lindblad F, Gustafsson PA, Larsson I, Lundin B. Preschoolers' sexual behavior at daycare centers: an epidemiological study. *Child Abuse Negl*. 1995;19:569-577.

10. Berkowitz CD. Medical consequences of child sexual abuse. *Child Abuse Negl*. 1998;22:541-50, discussion 551-554.

11. Monteleone JA. Sexual abuse. In: *A Parent's & Teacher's Handbook on Identifying and Preventing Child Abuse*. St. Louis, Mo: GW Medical Publishing;1998:49-57.

12. Kolilis GH. The role of law enforcement in the investigation of child maltreatment. In: Monteleone JA, ed. *Recognition of Child Abuse for the Mandated Reporter*. 2nd ed. St. Louis, Mo: GW Medical Publishing; 1996:161-170.

13. Kendall-Tackett K, Williams L, Finkelhor D. Impact of sexual abuse on children: a review and synthesis of recent empirical studies. *Psychol Bull*. 1993;113:164-180.

14. Paolucci EO, Genuis ML, Violato C. A meta-analysis of the published research on the effects of child sexual abuse. *J Psychol*. 2001;135:17-36.

15. McCann L, Pearlman LA, Sakheim DK, Abrahamson DJ. Assessment and treatment of the adult survivor of childhood sexual abuse within a schema of framework. In: Sgroi SM, ed. *Vulnerable Populations: Evaluation and Treatment of Sexually Abused Children and Adult Survivors*. Vol 1. Tortonto, Canada: Lexington Books; 1988:77-101.

16. Berlinger L, Elliott DM. Sexual Abuse of Children. In: Briere J, Berlinger L, Bulkley JA, Jenny C, Reid T, eds. *The APSAC Handbook on Child Maltreatment*. Thousand Oaks, Calif: Sage Publications; 1996.

17. Sgroi SM, Bunk BS. A clinical approach to adult survivors of child sexual abuse. In: Sgroi, SM, ed. *Vulnerable Populations*. Vol 1. New York, NY: Lexington Books; 1988.

18. Bachmann GA, Moeller TP, Benett J. Childhood sexual abuse and the consequences in adult women. *Obstet Gynecol*. 1988;71:631-642.

19. Jenny C, Sutherland SE, Sandahl BB. Developmental approach to preventing the sexual abuse of children. *Pediatrics*. 1986;78:1034-1038.

20. Whitman BY, Munkel W. Multiple personality disorder: a risk indicator, diagnostic marker and psychiatric outcome for severe child abuse. *Clin Pediatr (Phila)*. 1991;30:422-428.

21. Felitti VJ, Anda RF, Nordenberg D. Relationship of childhood abuse and household dysfunction to many of the leading causes of death in adults. The Adverse Childhood Experiences (ACE) Study. *Am J Prev Med*. 1998;14(4):245-58.

22. Summit RC. The child sexual abuse accommodation syndrome. *Child Abuse Negl*. 1983;7:177-193.

23. Summit R. Abuse of the child sexual abuse accommodation syndrome. *J Child Sex Abus*. 1992;1:153-163.

24. Finkelhor D, Brown A. The traumatic impact of child sexual abuse: a conceptualization. *Am J Orthopsychiatry*. 1985;55:530-541.

25. American Academy of Pediatrics Committee on Child Abuse and Neglect. Guidelines for the evaluation of sexual abuse of children: subject review. *Pediatrics*. 1999;103:186-191.

26. Nicholson EB, Bulkley J, eds. *Sexual Abuse Allegations in Custody and Visitation Cases: A Resource Book for Judges and Court Personnel*. Washington, DC: American Bar Association, National Legal Resource Center for Child Advocacy and Protection; 1988.

27. Paradise JE, Rostain AL, Natahnson M. Substantiation of sexual abuse charges when parents dispute custody or visitation. *Pediatrics*. 1988;81:835-839.

Chapter 4

EMOTIONAL ABUSE

Peggy S. Pearl, EdD
Angelo P. Giardino, MD, PhD, MPH, FAAP

Emotional abuse is probably the most difficult form of child abuse to identify and measure. This type of abuse goes further than the occasional yelling all parents may do. It includes severe acts that cause a child to become frightened, depressed, or violent. Examples include extreme levels of continual private and public ignoring, terrorizing, rejecting, humiliating, and more. Emotional abuse can often have deep and long-term effects on children, just like the other forms of abuse. The difficulty is that psychological wounds may be subtle, and they cannot simply be healed or reversed with the administration of medicine or physical care. Rather, for health development to proceed, an improved environment with caregivers who recognize the inherent value of the child is essential.

DEFINITIONS

Emotional abuse, sometimes called psychological abuse, involves intentionally hostile behavior as well as the absence of positive caregiving techniques. State laws typically define emotional abuse as a pattern of caregiving behavior that impairs a child's emotional development or sense of self-worth. The language used in these legal definitions often includes at least one of the following[1,2]:

— Damage to a child's psychological functioning or emotional stability

— Psychological injury evidenced by a substantial change in behavior, emotional response, or cognition

— Emotional instability evidenced by anxiety, depression, withdrawal, or aggressive behavior

This form of child maltreatment may include criticism, threats, or rejection. It may also include the withholding of love, support, or guidance. Emotional abuse is generally difficult to prove, and child protective services (CPS) agencies may not be able to intervene without obvious evidence of harm to the child.[1,2] Emotional abuse may or may not be a conscious act on the part of the caregivers, but the risk to children remains significant. Inevitably, it damages a child's psychological development and emerging personal identity.

Emotional abuse may inhibit the development of empathy, thereby impairing children's ability to appropriately give and receive emotions, sometimes severely. It has become clear that emotional abuse, such as lacking attachment, continually attacking a child's sense of worth, and failing to provide emotional nurturance, especially when coupled with neglect and perhaps early physical abuse, can impair children's capacity to respond to other people in a healthy emotional manner. When a child feels fear or distress, a capable caregiver normally responds with compassion, love, and physical comforting. These emotional, interactive responses are appropriate and form a core component of

55

"attachment." When caregivers do not respond in this way, but instead with repeated anger and rejection, attachment does not develop normally and children experience emotional abuse.[3,4]

In dysfunctional families, children may often experience multiple types of abuse and neglect. Some families treat—or mistreat—all children similarly, while others handle each child uniquely. The impact of emotional abuse on a child is varied and dependent on complex emotional and psychological factors. The timing of the emotional abuse relative to the child's developmental stage may influence the impact that the emotional abuse has on the child. For example, the earlier in a child's development that he or she experiences emotional abuse, the more damaging that experience may be since the child is deprived of the needed care and nurturance necessary to form an adequate self-image and sense of self-worth. On the other hand, if the the emotional abuse occurs later in the developmental process, after a child has had the opportunity to develop at least a basic level of self worth, then the child may be able to respond from a "more developed" position that may mitigate the negative impact of the abuse.

SIZE OF THE PROBLEM

Of the estimated 872 000 children who were determined to be victims of child abuse or neglect in 2004, 7% were identified as victims of emotional abuse.[5] This means that over 61 000 children experienced this form of abuse in that year alone (**Figure 4-1**).

Figure 4-1. In 2004, 7% of child maltreatment cases involved emotional abuse. Data from USDHHS.[5]

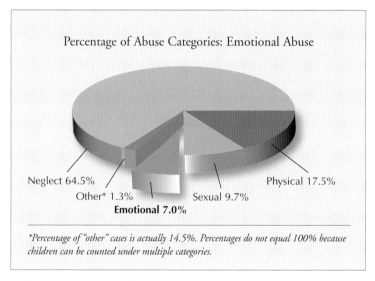

Percentage of Abuse Categories: Emotional Abuse

Neglect 64.5%
Other* 1.3%
Emotional 7.0%
Sexual 9.7%
Physical 17.5%

Percentage of "other" cases is actually 14.5%. Percentages do not equal 100% because children can be counted under multiple categories.

CAUSES OF EMOTIONAL ABUSE

Emotional abuse can take many forms, but all are rooted in the adult's struggle to have excessive control of the child. The younger a child is, and the less developed his or her senses of self and identity are, the more serious the physical, social, and emotional consequences that might result from emotional abuse will be. Emotional abuse may have less of an impact on older children who have a well-established sense of self than on younger or previously maltreated children.

Models of emotional abuse illustrate factors that can contribute to the formation of an abusive situation. Mentally ill parents or caregivers may be abusive, and mothers suffering from postpartum depression are often emotionally unavailable to their children. Children with more difficult needs to meet—for example, those with mental or physical disabilities—can stress parents beyond their coping abilities. Parents who are experiencing this or another form of stress or frustration and who do not have social supports, such as family, friends, or community support groups, may become emotionally abusive. Other adults must notice the mental health and life situation of parents for these factors to be recognized.

CHARACTERISTICS OF ABUSERS

Emotionally abusive caregivers tend to blame or belittle children in public, describe them in negative ways, consistently assume children are at fault, have developmentally or cognitively unrealistic expectations of children, freely admit to disliking or hating their child, threaten children with severe punishment, withdraw affection as a means of discipline, be emotionally cold and unsupportive, suffer from alcohol and drug abuse, and have a violent nature.[6] However, even though these characteristics are most commonly associated with emotionally abusive parents (**Table 4-1**), it is possible for nonabusive parents to possess some of them as well. If parents do show some of the above traits, it does not necessarily mean that they are or will become abusive. However, it may indicate that they have the potential to become so.

Table 4-1. Characteristics Common to Emotionally Abusive Caregivers

— Emotionally abused as children
— Stressed
— Lack of appropriate coping skills
— Mental illness (eg, schizophrenia, character disorder, depression)
— Angry
— Hostile
— Ambivalent toward parenthood
— Few resources (financial, social)
— Inappropriate expectations of children
— Lack of knowledge of normal child development
— Marital problems
— Lack of impulse control
— Chemically abusive
— Perpetuates domestic violence and/or knowingly allows child to live in violent home

Reprinted from Pearl.[7]

Summarized national reporting data on emotional maltreatment from the National Center on Child Abuse and Neglect (now the Child Welfare Information Gateway) indicated that parents were reported as perpetrators in 90% of reported cases of emotional abuse.[8] The gender distribution of reported cases indicated that women (57%) were slightly more likely to be reported than men (43%), and parents were most likely to be white.[8] These parents exhibited more psychosocial problems, more difficulty coping with stress, more difficulty building relationships, and more social isolation than did nonabusive parents. Abusive mothers lacked support networks and displayed greater levels of perceived stress, marital discord, and alcohol and drug use.[9] Although any type of abuse can occur in a home, regardless of its income level, families with annual incomes of less than $15 000 were significantly more likely to be reported for emotional maltreatment than families with higher incomes.[10]

Table 4-2. Ignoring Behaviors and Results	
Abusive Behaviors	— Not responding to a child's needs — Failing to appropriately stimulate children — Failing to look at children or call children by name — Failing to bond with children — Showing no affection for children — Being psychologically unavailable to children on a consistent basis
Resulting Characteristics	Studies done in the mid 1900s of ignored children in institutions describe socioemotional deprivation so severe that it was associated with infant mortality.[11] Most cases of maternal deprivation involving infants do not result in death because of medical intervention. Ignored children learn to live under the absolute control of adults who cannot be trusted. Children of mothers who were consistently emotionally unavailable show emotional and cognitive developmental delay.

Adapted from Pearl.[7]

TYPES OF EMOTIONAL ABUSE

IGNORING

Caregivers exhibiting *ignoring* behavior fail to acknowledge their child's presence or needs (**Table 4-2**). They are physically and psychologically unavailable to the child, whether on a consistent or an unpredictable basis. Ignoring is often part of serious physical neglect in which children's basic needs are not being tended. For example, the child may not be properly fed, clothed, sheltered, bathed, supervised, or acknowledged. Ignoring is an act of omission—passive and neglectful.

REJECTING

Rejecting occurs when caregivers refuse to touch or show affection to children and do not acknowledge children's presence or accomplishments (**Table 4-3**). Rejecting is an act of commission—active and abusive. These caregivers refuse to form attachments to their children during infancy, failing to respond to their infant's requests to have basic needs met or to their smiles and vocalizations of pleasure. As the child grows, the caregiver does not talk with the child or become involved in the preschooler's activities. Children of rejective caregivers are often not included in family activities and may spend long periods of time in solitary play, often in another room with the door closed, and their caregivers consistently communicate a negative definition of self to them. Such caregivers belittle children and their accomplishments, both privately and publicly, calling children names like "dummy," "clumsy," or "nerd." They have very low expectations of their children's performance in school, telling them that they cannot expect to pass or do well because they are not smart enough to succeed. A school-aged child or adolescent might be treated like a small child and not allowed to demonstrate age-appropriate levels of competence and independence. These caregivers do not acknowledge, and may even openly reject, the changes associated with adolescence, including social roles, physical size, sexual development, or increased cognitive ability. Children are told of their failures and are seldom, if ever, considered a valued individual within the family. Rejective caregivers commonly fail to have empathy for their children's needs.

Table 4-3. Rejective Behaviors and Results	
Abusive Behaviors	— Refusing to allow children to get needed psychological, medical, or educational services — Belittling and ridiculing children — Purposefully and continually embarrassing children — Singling children out for criticism and punishment — Failing to allow children to develop autonomy or independence — Undermining children's attachment to others — Routinely rejecting children's ideas — Ridiculing age-appropriate behaviors as too immature or punishing for them — Routinely calling children negative names — Routinely putting children down, publicly or privately — Inappropriately attributing undesirable characteristics to children — Denying children's needs and making them meet adult needs
Resulting Characteristics	Rejected children may be socially hostile and aggressive, have impaired self-esteem, and show either excessive dependency on parents and/or other adults or "defensive independence." They may appear emotionally unstable and unresponsive, eventually perceiving the world in negative terms. Children view themselves as having few strengths and skills and the world as being hostile and unwilling to assist them. They typically feel isolated and may in turn reject others.

Reprinted from Pearl.[7]

Rejective caregivers generally appear overwhelmed by a combination of social and economic hardships. Often, they are reacting to large families, limited material resources, limited education and job skills, and a lack of emotional and social supports, all of which stress them and limit their ability to nurture their children. These parents feel materially and psychologically unable to move beyond concern for themselves and into concern about their roles as caregivers, teachers, and providers of emotional support for their children. Examples of family circumstances that may be associated with an increased risk for rejection include:

— Unwanted pregnancies

— Lack of opportunity for caregivers to spend time alone

— Lack of paternal involvement in child rearing

— Marital discord

— Social isolation of family from the community

— Poor control or treatment of a caregiver's mental illness

ISOLATING

A variety of conditions can motivate a caregiver to display *isolating* behavior toward their children, but the effects it will produce are fairly consistent (**Table 4-4**). Generally, children who are isolated are prevented from having normal opportunities for social relations with both adults and peers. Some isolating caregivers are fearful of the outside world and are attempting to protect their children from the dangers they believe exist from contact with others. These families usually have a very limited amount of social contact, which deprives the children of learning social skills with a variety of individuals. Isolation can also be a characteristic of sexually abusive families and, in rare circumstances, families involved with ritualistic abuse. The isolation keeps what happens in the family a secret and prevents children from learning that there are other ways of life. Isolating caregivers lack social skills.

Table 4-4. Isolating Behaviors and Results	
Abusive Behaviors	— Not allowing children to participate in normal family routines — Not allowing children normal contact with peers — Physically separating children from the family unit — Not allowing children to participate in the social aspects of school — Routinely teaching children to avoid and distrust peers — Locking children in a bedroom, basement, or attic — Punishing requests for interaction with family or others — Binding or gagging children to prevent interaction — Refusing to allow children contact with noncustodial parent, grandparents, or siblings — Hiding children from the outside world
Resulting Characteristics	Children isolated for long periods of time lack the social competence to experience success or enjoyment in social situations, particularly in formal situations such as at school, and therefore do not like to attend such events, which further isolates them.

Reprinted from Pearl.[7]

TERRORIZING

Terrorizing involves threatening children with extreme or frightening punishment (**Table 4-5**). A caregiver intentionally stimulates intense fear, creates an unpredictable and threatening climate, or sets unattainable expectations and punishes the child for not attaining them. The disciplinary techniques are often arbitrary or beyond the child's ability to understand. Caregivers may tease or scare a young child in the name of humor. They may also discipline the child by playing on fears that are normal for that age, such as loud noises or the dark. In these cases, a terrorizing parent uses the feared situation to scare a child into behaving. For example, the parent may tell a preschool-aged child, "Monsters will drag you away in the night if you don't behave," or perhaps, "The night-light is watching, and if you're not good, it will zap you." Since adolescents tend to fear that their peers will see them as different or that they will not fit into social

---

Table 4-5. Terrorizing Behaviors and Results

Abusive Behaviors	— Threatening and frightening children with guns, knives, or whips — Making children feel excessively guilty — Behaving chaotically to frighten children — Laughing at or ridiculing children when they are frightened — Punishing children by playing on normal childhood fears — Disciplining children inconsistently and capriciously — Continually threatening suicide or abandonment — Threatening to harm others in children's presence — Knowingly permitting children to view or be involved in violent behavior — Routinely engaging in fights and frightening behavior in front of children — Failing to recognize the impact of domestic violence on children and failing to remove them from a violent environment — Binding or gagging children — Permitting others to terrorize children — Ritualistic abuse
Resulting Characteristics	Children become very anxious and will rarely initiate activities because they fear they will be criticized for any behavior.

Reprinted from Pearl.[7]

---

settings, a terrorizing caregiver may threaten an adolescent with public humiliation. Terrorized children often feel torn between a sense of loyalty and a sense of extreme fear and apprehension toward their caregivers. They want the abuse to end but also desire to be a part of the family; they long for affection and attention, yet they depend upon the people who are terrorizing them.

RITUALISTIC ABUSE

Ritualistic abuse is a form of terrorization in which children are systematically coerced into silence and participation in a ritual. It is the systematic, bizarre misuse of a child physically, socially, sexually, or emotionally by a group of adults and typically includes supernatural or religious activities. Ritualistic abuse is carefully integrated and classically linked with a symbol of overriding power, authority, and purpose, such as a religion or set of cult-like beliefs. In this unusual form of maltreatment, children may be involved in ceremonial sexual activity with adults, other children, or, to a lesser extent, animals. This activity is usually performed in front of other adults and children. Children might be bound, threatened, tortured, and drugged as part of the ritual. Some cases have also involved the force-feeding of human or animal feces, urine, blood, or flesh to children.[12]

CORRUPTING

Corrupting (**Table 4-6**) teaches and reinforces antisocial or deviant patterns that make children unable to function in a normal social setting. In milder forms, the caregivers encourage precocious interests or behaviors, such as those involving sexuality, aggression, violence, or substance abuse. Corruptive childrearing can begin with rewarding children for sexual contact (which is itself a form of sexual abuse), creating drug dependence, encouraging violence toward peers, or laughing at antisocial

---

Table 4-6. Corrupting Behaviors and Results

Abusive Behaviors	— Teaching or allowing others to teach children illegal or anti-social behaviors — Praising children for antisocial or delinquent behavior — Assisting children in delinquent behavior — Teaching children how to avoid consequences of anti-social or illegal behavior — Failing to discipline children for delinquent behavior — Teaching children that "bad is good and good is bad" — Giving drugs or other contraband to children — Exposing children to harmful influences or situations — Allowing and/or forcing children to watch pornographic materials — Teaching children sexually exploitative behaviors — Using children as spies, allies, or confidants in romantic relationships or marital or divorce problems — Failing to teach children socially appropriate and legal behaviors
Resulting Characteristics	Children risk developing antisocial behavior from an early age, though they may be unaware that their behavior is inappropriate. They may demonstrate a pseudomature behavior, unlike the normal behavior of age-mates, and be described as "street-smart kids." From a very young age, they demonstrate few positive emotions and are unable to play in an age-appropriate manner. They have a lack of respect for others that leads them to have no respect for themselves.

Reprinted from Pearl.[7]

---

behaviors. Other examples include allowing other adults to use their children for sexual activity, such as prostitution or child pornography, allowing children to sell or deliver drugs, and encouraging drug use.

In more serious forms of corrupting, the caregivers continue to encourage and reinforce the children's antisocial behavior as it grows more intense and destructive to self, others, or property. Ignoring delinquent behavior, rather than explicitly encouraging it, can have the same effect. Parents who knowingly allow children to engage in any illegal activity are corrupting those children. Corrupting also occurs when caregivers fail to teach their children the social skills necessary for successful interaction in the world around them, thus leaving them vulnerable to learning inappropriate behaviors from those who would take advantage of them.

VERBAL ASSAULT

Verbal assault involves constant name-calling, harsh threats, sarcastic put-downs, or other humiliation that lowers a child's sense of worth (**Table 4-7**). In an environment with verbal assault, words are tools of humiliation and control. Children are repeatedly told the things that they do wrong with little or no regard for what they do well, and they are often unfavorably compared with other family members or even downcast individuals. Caregivers regularly call children derogatory names. The verbal put-downs

Table 4-7. Verbally Assaulting Behaviors and Results	
Abusive Behaviors	— Continually attacking children verbally, especially in a loud voice — Failing to protect children from verbal attacks of others — Constantly belittling, criticizing, and humiliating children — Openly telling children that they are worthless and no good — Using children as scapegoats — Calling children derogatory or demeaning names — Cursing at children — Continually yelling at children — Falsely attributing negative behavior to children
Resulting Characteristics	Children may have a flat affect, low self-esteem, or self-mutilating behavior. They may be withdrawn and shy, and may demonstrate no sense of initiative. Children used as scapegoats are at high risk for childhood depression and suicide. Children have elevated rates of physical aggression, delinquency, and interpersonal problems. These children also describe having less enjoyment in life and more problems with sexual behavior, anger, and aggression.

Reprinted from Pearl.[7]

and attacks are usually delivered in a loud voice, further accenting their negativity, and can occur in private or in public. Such behavior is so pervasive among families who exhibit it that it is even routinely displayed when in the presence of childcare professionals. For these families, verbal assault is often an innate part of their very functioning as a family unit.

Professor Natalie Sachs-Ericsson and her colleagues recently studied 5614 people between the ages of 15 and 54 years and found that those who experienced verbal abuse had 1.6 times as many symptoms of depression and anxiety as those who did not and were also twice as likely to have suffered a mood or anxiety disorder over their lifetime.[13]

OVERPRESSURING
Overpressuring consistently occurs with parents who have inappropriately high expectations for their children (**Table 4-8**). Dr. David Elkind, in the now-classic book *The Hurried Child*, which has gone through 3 editions between 1981 and 2001, describes the tendency many parents have today of being more concerned about a child's intellectual achievements than his or her psychological well-being.[14] Children may be pushed to perform intellectual tasks early in order to prevent them from being considered "normal" or "average" in comparison to peers. Although this parental behavior is guided by the intention of facilitating children's cognitive development, it typically ends up actually impairing both cognitive and emotional development. Overpressuring may start with parents and caregivers trying to teach their children skills earlier than they should, whether it is toilet training, reading, counting, or working on computers. It can continue with inappropriate "pressuring and hurrying" throughout a child's life, as well as through parents holding unreasonably high expectations. Such caregivers may expect their children to graduate first in their class and consider graduating tenth to be a failure. They may also express disappointment when their child earns merely above-average standardized test scores. They will view consistently coming in second place in sports or other competitions as not really trying, whereas most

Table 4-8. Overpressuring Behaviors and Results

Abusive Behaviors	— Expressing unrealistically high expectations of children — Criticizing appropriate achievements by calling them inadequate — Punishing children for age-appropriate behavior by calling it "immature" — Ostracizing children for not possessing far-above-normal abilities — Not providing assistance with remedial work or acknowledging that assistance is even needed — Refusing to provide age-appropriate experiences; insisting on providing experiences that are too advanced — Beginning toilet training very early and insisting that children control body functions — Comparing children to those who are very advanced, consistently leaving children "poor by comparison" — Routinely buying toys that are far too advanced for children — Placing children in schools that are not appropriate for their ability
Resulting Characteristics	Overpressured children feel worthless, discouraged, lazy, unreliable, unacceptable, and inferior. They feel inadequate or unacceptable because parents are always trying to change them. Their identity is built in terms of accomplishments rather than based on an appreciation of self. Stress-related illnesses are common among these children. Because they lack parental support and good self-esteem, they are more vulnerable to negative experiences. These children may suffer from depression and are at high risk for eating disorders, suicide, and poor peer relationships throughout life.

Reprinted from Pearl.[7]

parents would consider that to be a good performance. Overpressured children are praised and valued when they accomplish something, but seldom for just being themselves and doing well.

OVEREXPOSURE TO COMMUNITY AND DOMESTIC VIOLENCE

Overexposure to community and domestic violence can have serious negative effects on children (**Table 4-9**). The degree to which it impacts a specific child varies with the length of time the child is exposed, the child's age and developmental stage, the level of social support received, and the presence of other stressors, such as poverty, homelessness, or substance abuse. Recent brain research has demonstrated that young children exposed to domestic violence experience brain changes that alter the way they process information. Exposure to chronic or extreme domestic and/or community violence may also result in symptoms consistent with posttraumatic stress disorder (PTSD). These symptoms include emotional numbing, increased arousal, avoidance of or obsessive focus on the violent event, depression, and violent behaviors.

Table 4-9. Overexposure to Violence Behaviors and Results

Abusive Behaviors	— Keeping children in a violent home or community — Acting violent in the presence of children — Allowing children to view violent and age-inappropriate media, including movies, television shows, and video games
Resulting Characteristics	Children may experience numbing, arousal, or depression or become irritable, immature, or distressed. They may believe that violence is an appropriate reaction to situations.

It is important to note that the negative impact of violence on children begins in infancy and is cumulative. Infants and toddlers who witness violence in their homes or community show excessive irritability, immature behavior, sleep disturbances, emotional distress, fears of being alone, and regression in both language and toileting control. Caregivers often deny that children of these ages even know the domestic violence is occurring. As young children continue to live with violence, they grow more anxious, experience more sleep disturbances, and have difficulty attending to required tasks and mastering age-appropriate skills. In school, they perform poorly, have emotional problems, experience difficulty with peers, and begin to engage in aggressive and delinquent behaviors.[15]

The terror of domestic violence forever changes the lives of children exposed to it, and the impact of the violence grows each time the cycle repeats. Estimates are that as many as 3.3 million US children are exposed to domestic violence each year.[16] These children are learning to settle disputes with violence and that it is okay to beat people one "loves." All too often, the movies, television shows, and video games children see reinforce these ideas. Many US children are being terrorized within their own homes, where they should instead be learning trust, security, and love.[15]

IDENTIFYING EMOTIONAL ABUSE

Emotional abuse is very difficult to isolate and identify. A complete picture may become evident as a child develops a trusting relationship with a therapist and begins to feel emotionally safe with professionals who can draw out his or her thoughts and feelings. When adults in the child's life notice the abnormal situation in which the child is being reared, the opportunity arises to identify the potential emotional risk to which the child is being exposed. Professionals and laypeople alike need to be willing to report these risky situations to the appropriate authorities in order to intervene on behalf of the children at risk. Emotional abuse generally results in reduced cognitive and emotional function. Identifying the former is more easily accomplished than identifying the latter, but both of these impairments can help alert professionals that a child is a victim of emotional abuse. Also, although both impairments do typically appear concurrently, it should not be assumed that emotional abuse will necessarily reduce cognitive ability.

BEHAVIORAL INDICATORS

Emotionally abused children may exhibit a wide range of behaviors, including apathy, crying and irritability, refusing to be calmed, and avoiding eye contact with parents or other adults. According to Prevent Child Abuse America (PCA America), indicators that a child may be emotionally abused include unusually mature or immature behavior, dramatic behavioral changes, compulsive seeking of affection and attention, aggressiveness, uncooperativeness, new onset of or increased bedwetting or loss of bowel control (when the child has already been trained), and possibly destructive or antisocial behavior. Other indicators include poor peer relationships, a lack of self-confidence, fears unusual for a child's age, or an inability to react with emotion or develop an emotional bond with others.[6]

Children who externalize their feelings tend to be disobedient, impulsive, and over-active. They lack self-control and are often violent toward other people and their environment. Maltreated children who are aggressive exhibit continuous and generalized aggression, behaving according to impulses rather than social norms. The aggression is a state of being rather than a response to a specific action or individual. Abused children who internalize their feelings are withdrawn, indifferent, submissive, and hostile.

Some indicators of emotional abuse in children may include:

— Difficulty in forming relationships

— An inability to relate and bond to other children

— Lack of self-confidence and emotion

— Extreme shyness

— Being victimized and exploited by other children

— Fatigue and listlessness

— Helplessness and hopelessness

— Feelings of inadequacy

— Pessimism and preoccupation

— Difficulty concentrating on school activities

— Self-denial

— An inability to engage in and enjoy pleasurable activities

— Self-injury (hair pulling and twisting, nail biting, accident prone)

Children who respond aggressively to emotional abuse may engage in the following behaviors[17]:

— Bullying or hostility toward others

— Intimidating and threatening others

— Ridiculing others

— Cruelty to other children and animals

— Destruction of property and/or fire setting

— Repeated truancy or tardiness

— Constant attention seeking and hyperactivity

PASSIVITY

Emotional abuse can make children numb to environmental stimuli. When left alone with familiar objects, they may not have normal, age-appropriate play skills, or they may not demonstrate pleasure and satisfaction from either solitary play or play with adults. They are excessively passive and obedient. Emotionally maltreated infants may manifest a flat affect. They may fail to grimace or show pain when appropriate, such as not crying after a fall or an injection. They may also not respond as other children would when toys, food, or other items are taken away from them. In situations where a normal child would cry or seek comfort, these children may appear indifferent.

NEGATIVE SELF-IMAGE

Young abused children demonstrate a negative view of their world and selves. They feel unworthy and consider the world a hostile place. They are fearful, angry, anxious, aggressive, and sometimes violent, and they may engage in both physically and socially self-destructive behavior. They are often depressed, withdrawn, passive, and shy, exhibiting poor interpersonal communication skills and, in some cases, becoming suicidal. They may frequently complain of physical conditions such as headaches or sleep disturbances.

ABNORMAL RESPONSES

Some emotionally maltreated children display hesitant response patterns or low levels of social responsiveness. They approach unfamiliar adults indiscriminately, seeking attention but avoiding physical contact with them, or cling to adults other than their parents and remain distant from peers. In either instance, children's social behavior can be situationally inappropriate. Generally, children are unable to respond to environmental rewards, such as smiles, verbal praise, or peers asking them to join group activities. Children are often indifferent to positive feedback about their successes and respond negatively to social challenges or peer rejection.

PSYCHOLOGICAL MODELS

Several scientific models have been suggested to try to explain how emotionally abusive situations develop. Among the more common approaches are the psychiatric approach, the social approach, and the human ecological approach.

THE PSYCHIATRIC APPROACH

The *psychiatric approach* to emotional abuse assumes that the perpetrating adult suffers from some mental illness. A relatively small number of all maltreating caregivers are severely mentally ill and have an antisocial personality. Mentally ill parents are at high risk for failing to meet a child's psychological needs because of the amount of effort they must expend to meet their own emotional needs. As compared to non–mentally ill caregivers, emotionally abusive caregivers tend to have significantly more psychosocial problems, more difficulty coping with stress, more difficulty building relationships, and more social isolation. A mother who is psychologically stressed and overwhelmed with her own depression after childbirth likely lacks the physical or emotional energy to give her child what he or she needs. A caregiver preoccupied with the death of a parent, sibling, or spouse may also be unable to meet a child's needs. Although postpartum depression and grief tend to be short and reversible, they still negatively impact the parent-child relationship and can adversely affect the developing child. Caregivers' mental illness explains only a small number of emotional abuse cases.

THE SOCIAL APPROACH

The *social approach* theory places emphasis on the role of stress as a force impacting family dynamics and causing emotional abuse. In this approach, social stress interacting with other variables leads to aggression in the form of emotional abuse. Family stressors include limited resources, problems at work, death of a significant other, unemployment, health problems, overcrowding, isolation, substance abuse, high levels of mobility, poverty, and marital problems. All caregivers experience some forms of stress, but different people respond to stress in different ways. The following mediating variables can assist in identifying how likely a caregiver is to abuse his or her children:

— Presence or lack of appropriate coping mechanisms

— Degree of family integration or isolation

— Presence or lack of positive social networks

Women tend toward depression as a response to stress, whereas men tend to respond with violence. Stressed women usually are psychologically unavailable to their children, consequently ignoring, rejecting, or isolating them. Stressed men, on the other hand, tend to physically or verbally assault their children. Mediating variables and the underlying causes of the stress determine the length and degree of the emotional abuse and, consequently, the amount of damage to the child's development.

THE HUMAN ECOLOGICAL APPROACH

The *human ecological approach* of emotional abuse involves all aspects of a family's life and the surrounding community. Parents bring various influences to the parent-child relationship, including their marital experiences, how they understand and implement their roles as caregivers, and their relationships with their own caregivers. In the case of remarriage, new values, beliefs, and histories are introduced, and it is necessary for each family member to adapt. How each caregiver was raised also plays a significant role in determining what parenting skills they possess and will use. The mental health and range of social abilities of all individuals in the family will play an important role in the choices and actions of both caregivers and children. A child may have a history that does not involve his or her parents; perhaps the child was reared by a grandmother for the first 3 years of life, or one parent was away in the military or working for an extended period of time. Children's health, temperament, gender, ordinal position in the family, and level of family bonding are also critical aspects of the human ecological theory that can influence parenting choices and actions.

In families, children are often parented uniquely, based in part on the temperament, personality, and individual ability of each child. Verbally assaulting a strong-willed child may seem justified to caregivers who lack the knowledge and temperament to work with the child. Other caregivers may ignore a child with challenging behaviors, failing to provide adequate emotional nurturing, guidance, and recognition of his or her needs. Children with special needs are sometimes ignored, rejected, isolated, and verbally assaulted because their caregiver is inadequately skilled to provide for those needs.

Economic and geographic changes also influence the parent-child relationship. Voluntary or involuntary job changes can introduce stress on the family that tends to yield negative effects. Each family varies in its social context and support system. A high degree of family isolation and a lack of resources dramatically influences parenting values and abilities. If a family moves to another town, parents may lose the social support system of relatives and friends that helped them care for their children. They may also have to adapt to a lower level of community resources. It is important to recognize that isolation and lack of resources will vary throughout anyone's life. Still, these ecological aspects may heighten stress levels within a family and lead to abuse.

Society, too, influences parental choices and actions. Does the local community offer general acceptance of individual differences or does it demand conformity? Are children or adolescents terrorized into conforming when they question adult authority and beliefs? The answers to these questions will identify critical influences that the community or society may have on parenting choices. In short, the interaction of all the influencing child-parent-family-societal factors helps determine the type of parenting exhibited by caregivers.

IMPACT OF EMOTIONAL ABUSE

Consequences of abuse vary with each child's age, relationship to the abuser, and level of development at the time of the abuse. The consequences of maltreatment can be observed in the child's behaviors as they progresses through different developmental stages. Behavioral disorders and delays in development of motor skills appear at all ages. Research has related psychologically unavailable caregivers and verbally hostile caregivers to the development of child deviance and delay.[12]

Caregivers who ignore and reject children's basic needs appear to raise children who are destructive, impulsive, low in ego control, passive, less flexible, less creative, less persistent, and avoidant of their mothers. Young children who have experienced parental rejection often exhibit symptoms in the early preschool years, when they have difficulty controlling aggression, respond inappropriately to distress in others, and exhibit self-isolating tendencies. Young children lack the self-esteem and trust necessary to explore the environment or attend to cognitively-oriented tasks. Most individuals tend to view themselves as they believe "significant others" view them, and, because parents are typically the most significant others of young children, children who are rejected by their parents see themselves as unworthy of love and inadequate as individuals. This negativity makes children less tolerant of stress, less emotionally stable, more emotionally insulated, more dependent, more possessive, more defensive, more emotionally detached, and angrier. Other possible consequences are:

— Psychiatric disorders (depression, character disorder, borderline personality disorder, multiple personality disorder, attention deficit disorder).

— Violent behavior, especially toward family members.

— Increased vulnerability.

— Delayed development of language, cognitive, and motor skills.

— Decreased exploratory activity.

— Relationship problems.

— Low self-esteem.

— Sleep disorders.

— Eating disorders.

— Poor growth or failure to thrive.

— Learned helplessness.

TREATMENT AND SERVICES

Few interventions or treatment services are uniquely designed for emotional maltreatment. Most families with a variety of problems need multiservice interventions, including a combination of the following: individual, group, and family counseling; social support services; behavioral skills training; and parenting education, including family safety, accident prevention, and nutrition. Children from these environments may also need developmentally appropriate educational services, such as speech and language therapy, motor skills development, and environmental enrichment. Children who have experienced emotional maltreatment need a careful medical evaluation to ensure that medical problems do not exist in combination with psychological problems. Because children with disabilities are overly represented among the children identified in CPS, the treatment team must carefully observe the child.

Table 4-10. American Humane Association's "What You Can Do"

All children need acceptance, love, encouragement, discipline, consistency, stability, and positive attention. What can you do when you feel your behavior toward your child is not embodying these qualities but is bordering on emotional abuse? Here are some suggestions:

— Never be afraid to apologize to your child. If you lose your temper and say something in anger that was not meant to be said, apologize. Children need to know that adults can admit when they are wrong.

— Do not call your child names or attach labels to your child. Names such as "stupid," "lazy," and "good-for-nothing" should be avoided. So too should the phrases, "You'll never amount to anything," "If you could only be more like your brother," and "You can never do anything right." All of these can tear at a child's self-esteem. A child deserves respect.

— Address the behavior that needs correcting and use appropriate disciplinary techniques, such as time-outs or natural consequences. Be sure to discuss the child's behavior and the reason for the discipline, both before and immediately after you discipline. Discipline should be provided to correct your child's behavior, not to punish or humiliate him or her.

— Compliment your child when he or she accomplishes even a small task, or when you see good behavior.

— Recognize when you are losing control and temporarily remove yourself from the situation before you overreact. Isolate yourself in another room for a few minutes (after first making sure the child is safe), count to 10 before you say anything, ask for help from another adult, or take a few deep breaths before reacting.

— Get help. Support is available for families at risk of emotional abuse through local child protection services agencies, community centers, churches, physicians, mental health facilities, and schools.

Adapted from American Humane Association.[18]

Research continues on the effectiveness of specific interventions for all types of child abuse and neglect. However, treatment of emotional abuse is underrepresented in the outcome literature. As resources for intervention diminish in the public sector, more information is needed on how to most effectively use the limited resources.

PCA America advises that in order to effectively identify and confirm emotional abuse, it is necessary to observe the abuser-child interaction on different occasions. If emotional abuse is suspected, seeking help for the child is essential and action needs to be taken, regardless of whether the suspected perpetrator is part of the child's home, in the childcare setting, or somewhere else in the neighborhood. It is the concerned adult's responsibility to seek help and report the suspected abuse, not to prove the suspicion. The goal remains to get the child help and the nurturing type of care they need.[6] **Table 4-10** lists some simple recommendations for helping make the children around us feel cared for.

CONCLUSION

Emotional abuse may cause children to experience impairment in all areas of development. The impairment is minimized when children are able to form secure attachments to caregivers in their environment, when the abuse is not combined with other forms of maltreatment, and when the abuse is mild or occurs only over a short period of time. However, in most cases, some long-term impairment is expected in various areas of development. Children are likely to have lower self-esteem and may enjoy life less, becoming either withdrawn and passive or aggressive and hostile. Cognitive and language development may also be delayed, as may physical growth and motor abilities. Identifying children who are being emotionally abused early and providing them with a supportive environment and nurturance are essential steps toward helping children overcome the negative effects of emotional abuse.

REFERENCES

1. Goldman J, Salus MK, Wolcott D, Kennedy KY. *A Coordinated Response to Child Abuse and Neglect: The Foundation for Practice*. Washington, DC: Office on Child Abuse and Neglect, US Dept of Health & Human Services; 2003. Available at: http://www.nccanch.acf.hhs.gov/pubs/usermanuals/foundation/foundation.pdf. Accessed June 30, 2006.

2. Child Welfare Information Gateway. *Definitions of Child Abuse and Neglect*. Washington, DC: Child Welfare Information Gateway; 2005. State Statutes Series.

3. Garbarino J, Guttmann E, Seeley JW. *The Psychologically Battered Child: Strategies for Identification, Assessment, and Intervention*. San Francisco, Calif: Jossey-Bass, Inc; 1987.

4. Wolfe DA. *Preventing Physical and Emotional Abuse of Children*. New York, NY: Guilford Press; 1991.

5. US Department of Health & Human Services, Administration on Children, Youth and Families. *Child Maltreatment 2004*. Washington, DC: US Government Printing Office; 2006. Available at: http://www.acf.hhs.gov/programs/cb/pubs/cm04/index.htm. Accessed July 1, 2006.

6. Prevent Child Abuse America. *Fact Sheet: Emotional Child Abuse*. Available at: http://member.preventchildabuse.org/site/DocServer/emotional_child_abuse.pdf?docID=122. Accessed May 25, 2006.

7. Pearl PS. Psychological abuse. In: Giardino AP, Giardino ER. *Recognition of Child Abuse for the Mandated Reporter*. 3rd ed. St. Louis, Mo: GW Medical Publishing; 2002.

8. US Department of Health & Human Services. *Study Findings: Study of National Incidence and Prevalence of Child Abuse and Neglect*. Washington, DC: Government Printing Office; 1988. DHHS Publication NO. ADM 20-01099.

9. Hickox A, Furnell JR. Psychosocial and background factors in emotional abuse of children. *Child Care Health Dev*. 1989;15:227-240.

10. Sedlak AJ, Broadhurst DD. *Third National Incidence Study of Child Abuse and Neglect (NIS-3 Final Report)*. Washington, DC: US Dept of Health & Human Services; 1996. Contract No. 105-94-1840.

11. Spitz RA. Hospitalism: an inquiry into the genesis of psychiatric conditions in children. In: Eissler RS, ed. *The Psychoanalytic Study of the Child*. Vol 1. New York, NY: International Universities Press: 1945:53-74.

12. Young WC, Sachs RG, Braun BG, Watkins RT. Patients reporting ritual abuse in childhood: a clinical syndrome report of 37 cases. *Child Abuse Negl*. 1991;15:181-189.

13. Elish J. Verbal abuse in childhood triggers adult anxiety, depression. *Medical News Today*. May 24, 2006:Psychology/psychiatry section. Available at: http://www.medicalnewstoday.com/medicalnews.php?newsid=43894&nfid=crss. Accessed July 1, 2006.

14. Elkind D. *The Hurried Child: Growing Up Too Fast Too Soon.* 3rd ed. Reading, Mass: Addison-Wesley Publishing Co; 2001.

15. Osofsky JD. The impact of violence on children. *Future Child.* 1999;9:33-49.

16. American Academy of Pediatrics Committee on Child Abuse and Neglect. The role of pediatricians in recognizing and intervening on behalf of abused women. *Pediatrics.* 1998;101:1091-1092.

17. Romeor FF. The educator's role in reporting the emotional abuse of children. *J Instr Psychol.* 2000;27(3):183-186.

18. Child fact sheets: emotional abuse. American Humane Association Web site. Available at: http://www.americanhumane.org/site/PageServer?pagename=nr_fact_sheets_childemotionalabuse. Accessed July 1, 2006.

Chapter 5

Child Neglect

Angelo P. Giardino, MD, PhD, MPH, FAAP

Child neglect is a major concern. It accounts for approximately half of all child maltreatment cases and more than half of all deaths from child maltreatment. Neglect often develops gradually and may go undetected for a significant amount of time. Unfortunately, neglect is often not detected until it is too late. It is extremely important for caregivers and other adults to be able to recognize the symptoms of neglect. Once it is discovered, we can spare children from further neglect and help them physically and mentally recover by placing them in therapeutic environments.

Definitions

Neglect is typically defined as a caregiver presenting a risk of serious physical or emotional harm to a child by failing to act on his or her behalf. Legally, neglect is a failure to provide a child with adequate food, clothing, shelter, supervision, safety, or medical care. Some legal definitions for neglect include child abandonment as a subcategory, though others define it separately. ***Child abandonment*** occurs when parents' identities or whereabouts are unknown to those left caring for the child. Often, caregivers leave children in places that are harmful, or they fail to maintain contact with the child or provide reasonable support for an extended period of time. Classically, definitions of neglect discuss acts of omission that place the child at risk of being harmed, whereas definitions of abuse discuss acts of commission where the child actually is harmed.

For clinicians and teachers, child neglect is a failure on the part of the caregiver to meet a child's basic needs, which include the following[1]:

— Food

— Warmth

— Clothing

— Shelter and protection

— Grooming and hygiene

— Fresh air and sunlight

— Activity and rest

— Prevention of illness

— Prevention of accidents

— Affection

— Continuity of care

— Security of belonging

— A sense of self-esteem

— Opportunities to learn

There are 5 forms of neglect: medical, physical, safety, educational, and emotional. Dr. Susan Zuravin further divided these 5 basic categories into 12 subcategories[2]:

1. Refusal or delay in providing physical health care

2. Refusal or delay in providing mental health care

3. Supervisory neglect

4. Custody refusal

5. Custody-related neglect

6. Abandonment/desertion

7. Failure to provide a stable home

8. Neglect of personal hygiene

9. Housing hazards

10. Inadequate housing sanitation

11. Nutritional neglect

12. Educational neglect

SIZE OF THE PROBLEM

Neglect is the most common form of child maltreatment and a major threat to the health and well-being of children, as more than 560 000 children experienced neglect in 2004 alone. Even with yearly variation, the number of cases of neglect per year is approximately twice the number of physical abuse and approximately 4 times the number of sexual abuse (**Figure 5-1**). Data from 2004 show 65% of child maltreatment cases involved neglect, while 18% of cases involved physical abuse and another 10% involved sexual abuse.[3] Child neglect is not benign and, regretfully, over half the child deaths attributed to caregivers are found to be a result of neglect.

Figure 5-1. *In 2004, 64.5% of child maltreatment cases involved sexual abuse. Data from USDHHS.*[3]

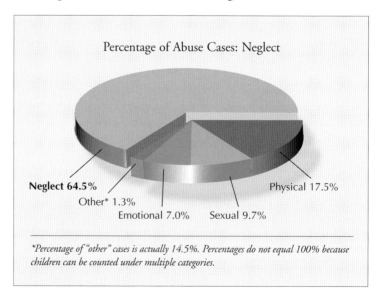

Percentage of Abuse Cases: Neglect

Neglect 64.5%
Other* 1.3%
Emotional 7.0%
Sexual 9.7%
Physical 17.5%

*Percentage of "other" cases is actually 14.5%. Percentages do not equal 100% because children can be counted under multiple categories.

CAUSES OF NEGLECT

Neglect is often lumped together with child abuse or more generally with child maltreatment, suggesting that its risk factors, modes, and outcomes are similar. However, child neglect is a separate, unique form of child maltreatment and differs from child abuse in many ways. Parents and caregivers who neglect their children typically are less involved and less interested in their children and have more negative interactions with them than do abusing parents and caregivers. For example, mothers who neglect their children have lower perceptions of their own personal and social abilities and lower self-esteem than physically abusive mothers.[4] Several studies have even observed that being a victim of child neglect may be more damaging to a child's development than being a victim of physical abuse. Neglect and emotional abuse may have a significantly higher number of negative long-term effects on a child's academic performance, psychological distress, and psychiatric issues than physical abuse. The all-encompassing nature of child neglect in the life and developmental well-being of a child, and its connection to having basic needs left unmet, seems to be especially destabilizing and destructive to a child's growth, social development, and ability to learn.

The scientific view of neglect has evolved over time, and professionals have shifted from using psychiatric models, which focus on blaming deficient parents, to the human ecological model, which focuses more on the factors that come together to create a situation of neglect. As described in Chapter 1, Child Abuse and Neglect: An Overview of the Problem, the human ecological model views the family as being a "system" that operates within other larger systems, and it seeks to define a shared responsibility that identifies factors influencing the caregivers' ability to provide appropriate care.[5]

Put simply, child neglect is now primarily understood as the result of a mismatch between child and family, as well as between family and neighborhood or the broader community. Neglectful families are essentially isolated in their environment due to a lack of available supportive relationships (either real or perceived) in the neighborhood or community that would, if present, function as a source of nurturance and feedback.[6,7] For a variety of reasons, neglectful parents and caregivers do not seem capable of developing the necessary connections to form these relationships with other, non-neglectful parents.

Neglect can also be viewed as a pattern of caregivers who cannot effectively use knowledge, support, and resources to carry out their caregiving role.[8] Viewing neglect as a faulty pattern of learned caregiving that can be modified with support and training, rather than as an inherent parental deficit, renders neglect a problem that positive action can solve. The solution lies in finding whatever strengths a family might have, no matter how slight, and then building an intervention on top of those strengths to address some of the family's weaknesses. The goal of people and programs working with neglectful situations is to help children by offering support and services to caregivers that will help them better meet their children's basic needs.[9]

TYPES OF CHILD NEGLECT

MEDICAL NEGLECT

Children's health care needs do vary, but all children need regular checkups and immunizations. Children with diseases or conditions that cannot be cured often have special medical care needs. When a child is medically neglected, caregivers may not obtain minimal health care or immunizations for the child. Often, caregivers rely either too little or too much on emergency services. They may ignore dental needs, fail to obtain prescribed medicines or equipment, or fail to follow treatment for a chronic physical or mental illness. When law and religion intersect over issues such as immunizations, blood products, pain medications, or other specific treatments, legal provisions generally favor having the court intervene on behalf of the child. An illness or injury that is not receiving care and is becoming a chronic problem is a signal of medical neglect.

PHYSICAL NEGLECT

Nutrition

Children require food that meets their nutritional needs and is appropriate for their age and stage of development. Children may suffer when they have food that is poor quality, nonnutritious, or from only some of the food groups. For example, it is not healthy for a child to have too many carbohydrates or sweets and not enough vegetables, meats, fresh fruits, or dairy products. The child's age and level of development are important to consider since children's nutritional needs change over time. Preparing meals consistently is another important part of meeting a child's nutritional needs. And not only should caregivers provide the right types of food, they should also make mealtime itself a pleasant experience. In some homes, meals can be chaotic and stressful, which is not an ideal situation.

Certain signals can help identify whether a child's nutritional needs are being neglected. If a child is always asking for food, has the same nonnutritious lunch every day, or appears too thin, there may be a problem.

Clothing

Children need clothing that is adequate and appropriate for the current weather and season. If children's clothing is dirty, does not fit well, or is torn or worn out, they may suffer from exposure to the natural elements such as rain or the cold. Shoes must be adequate for the season, of the right size, and in good shape. Outerwear is also important: Raincoats or umbrellas are necessary for rainy weather; heavy coats, hats, and gloves are vital for protection in the winter. If a child continually lacks appropriate clothing, be concerned.

Personal Hygiene

As children grow, they need to be taught personal hygiene and given tools for self-care. Children who have not bathed for a long time usually smell of urine, feces, or sweat, are encrusted with dirt, and/or have unkempt hair. Poor dental hygiene can also result in severe dental cavities and mouth odor. Children with poor hygiene are almost certainly neglected.

SUPERVISORY OR SAFETY NEGLECT

Lack of supervision is a serious form of neglect. Children may suffer repeated injury simply because a caregiver is not paying adequate attention to what they are doing. They must be protected from household dangers such as open windows, stairs, electrical wiring, and any other items that have the potential to cause an injury. Caregivers should also take measures to ensure that children do not get into toxic substances or medications and suffer accidental poisoning.

There is no national standard regarding the age at which children can be left unsupervised, but many state laws specify it as 12 years of age. More basically, children who cannot care for themselves must be supervised. As children get older, they can be left alone for longer periods of time.

Inadequate Shelter

Children need a home that provides shelter so that their other basic needs can be met.

The standards for what is adequate vary from community to community, but the minimums include:

— Shelter from the elements.

— Heating in cold weather.

— Adequate space for sleeping, eating, bathing, and playing.

In houses that are crowded with people, furnishings, clutter, or trash, the physical and safety needs of the children may simply be too difficult to meet. In such a disorganized environment, children may not be supervised because each adult, in the midst of the disarray, may assume that someone else is managing the child's care at that time.

Unsanitary Conditions

Houses in which clutter and trash are allowed to accumulate are unsafe and unsanitary for children. Any space can become temporarily cluttered, but it is the neglectful caregiver who makes no attempt to clean up or remove the mess. In extreme situations, toilets may be unusable, and animal or human waste may be on the floors. Unsanitary houses may be infested with rats, mice, or roaches, further contributing to the unhealthiness of the environment.

Structural Hazards

Houses that are not properly maintained can develop structural hazards, which put children's safety at risk. Examples of structural hazards include:

— A house or building that has partially collapsed.

— Stairways that have broken steps.

— Stairways, porches, or balconies that have missing railings or missing protective barriers.

— Windows and doors that are in poor repair, including those with broken or jagged glass.

— Doors or window screens that are missing entirely.

— Floors or ceilings that have holes.

— Floors that are badly worn with large splinters.

Fire Hazards

Common fire hazards include exposed or frayed wiring, fuel containers stored in living areas, and combustible materials placed near heat sources. When beds are placed too close to heat sources, the heat can burn children or set the beds on fire. Metal bars on windows are also unsafe, as are difficult-to-release door bolts, because they will trap people inside if a house is on fire.

Substance Accessibility and Use

Leaving chemicals or drugs in a place that is accessible to children is neglectful. Having illicit drugs in the house and using the house for drug-trafficking crimes are particularly hazardous when children are around. Each year, thousands of children are poisoned when they ingest household chemicals or drugs in their homes or the homes of other people.[10]

Excessive Hot Water Temperature

Children are burned by excessively hot water. The scenarios caregivers relate are remarkably similar: The bath water is turned on, the caregiver leaves the bathroom for "just a minute," and suddenly he or she hears the child's cries coming from the bathroom. After rushing back to the bathroom, the caregiver finds the child with severe second-degree burns. To avoid situations like this, make sure the hot water setting in your house does not exceed 49°C (120°F) and that you never leave a young child unsupervised in the bathtub or in a bathroom when the bathtub is filled.

EDUCATIONAL NEGLECT

According to state law, children must be enrolled in school between certain ages, usually 7 and 16 years. Nevertheless, some caregivers permit chronic truancy and do not encourage children to attend school. The caregiver may also fail to provide control and discipline or fail to model learning, socialization, and responsible behavior. When homeschooling, parents are required to work within the laws of their state. If children are frequently late to, absent from, or unenrolled in school, they may be neglected.

IDENTIFYING CHILD NEGLECT

Neglect tends to exist "below the surface" of family life and often establishes itself gradually. Unless a tragedy occurs, like the death or serious injury of an unsupervised child, it is easy for a neglect case to go unreported and even undetected. Some neglect cases do receive media attention, but it is generally only the extreme ones—the homes with garbage heaped to the point of covering furniture, human and animal waste overflowing from broken toilets, rat droppings on stale or moldy food, and children wearing only t-shirts in below-freezing weather. Although these graphic images do call attention to the problem, they do not illustrate typical cases. Often, neglect takes much more subtle forms.

Determining whether neglect is chronic or recent in onset is important because it will guide the design of the intervention. It is important to note that the term "neglect" takes into account both culture and social class and therefore varies in meaning for different groups of people. As an example, the minimum age at which a child is expected to be able to care for a toddler is lower for some ethnic groups than others. In some cultures, the older children in the families are trained in basic safety skills and so are able to care for younger siblings. Extended family members, neighbors, and friends also play larger roles in childcare and supervision for some ethnic groups than others. Cultural values and practices not only influence care of the children but also set standards for the size, structure, and physical condition of housing, as well as for the furniture and appliances therein. Particular communities and ethnic groups have limited housing options. The unavailability of adequate low-rent housing becomes a question of community neglect, rather than child neglect. In some cases, it may seem that caregivers are being neglectful, when in fact they are merely struggling with what meager resources are available to them.

The National Clearinghouse on Child Abuse and Neglect (NCCAN) and Prevent Child Abuse America (PCA America) describe signs that may indicate the presence of child neglect. Your suspicions should be aroused if a child[11]:

— Is frequently absent from school.

— Begs for or steals food or money.

— Lacks needed medical or dental care, immunizations, or glasses.

— Is consistently dirty and has severe body odor.

— Lacks sufficient clothing for the weather.

— Abuses alcohol or other drugs.

— States that there is no one at home to provide care.

Additionally, child neglect should be considered when the parent or other adult caregiver:

— Appears to be indifferent to the child.

— Seems apathetic or depressed.

— Behaves irrationally or in a bizarre manner.

— Is abusing alcohol or other drugs.

The following case demonstrates what can happen in a situation where extreme neglect and abandonment is discovered.

CASE EXAMPLE

A 2-year-old boy darted into the street to catch up with his 4-year-old sister and 6-year-old brother. They were late for the preschool they attended. The child, in his haste, did not see the approaching ambulance, which soon ran over and broke his feet. When he was brought to the emergency room, a hospital social worker recognized the boy's mother from previous clinic visits. Her children were already being treated for lead poisoning, and her infant had been treated 3 times in recent weeks for rat bites. Sensing that these patterns might be indicative of a larger problem, the social worker called child protective services (CPS) to report a lack of parental supervision.

CPS workers soon performed an investigation of the family's home, during which they discovered a lack of appropriate heat, electricity, and running water. The only available electricity was being stolen from a neighbor's apartment through a series of small-gauge extension cords. The only source of heat was a single hot plate. Investigators also discovered a nest of live rats under the kitchen sink, along with several of its members skittering around the kitchen floor. The rodents' footprints could clearly be seen on the leftover food on the kitchen table. The entire apartment smelled of sewage. Investigators found a bathroom in which both the tub and toilet were not functioning, yet still being used. The overflow from the tub and toilet had created a black, tarry substance that covered the floor.

The children living in the home appeared malnourished and had clearly not bathed in a long time. All 3 had head lice, and their hair had not been combed or brushed in weeks. Their clothing was dirty and torn, and it was obvious that the children were cold.

The children were taken into protective custody. As the investigators were leaving, they heard an infant cry. Using flashlights, they found the infant in a pile of rags in a darkened room. The infant had rat bites that required medical attention.

It was later discovered that though the mother was clearly failing to provide for her children, she did possess an income that was sufficient to do so. She was charged with neglect, convicted, and then placed on probation. The children remained in foster care for several years, until they were eventually able to be safely cared for by members of their biological family.

HEALTH CARE EVALUATION

The standard primary care health care evaluation consists of a history, a physical examination, laboratory and imaging studies as needed, and observations of parent-child interaction. These components will typically be completed on all routine check-ups, called "well-child visits." Because there are many categories and subcategories of neglect, and because professional recognition of child neglect tends to develop over time, it is important to see each health care visit as a general opportunity to screen for children's overall health and well-being.

If any specific concerns arise from the general screening, or if a worrisome pattern develops over time, then the health care professional can add more specific questions and examinations to explore these concerns further. **Table 5-1** lists some of the specific information that the health care professional might seek if the general visit raises concerns for a specific category of neglect.

IMPACT OF CHILD NEGLECT

Neglect has far-reaching effects on children, influencing the development of their physical, psychological, intellectual, social, behavioral, and emotional health.[12] The impact of neglect on an individual child depends on many factors, including the child's

---

Table 5-1. Issues Questioned During Health Care Evaluations When Neglect Is Suspected

MEDICAL NEGLECT

History
Examine the appropriateness of the caregiver's response, including:
— Timeliness for routine care.
— Response to presence of symptoms.
— Reported adherence to medical regimens.
— Expression of concern and interest.

Physical examination
Assess:
— General appearance, looking for signs of neglect.
— Delays in seeking treatment for new symptoms:
    — What are the findings?
    — How obvious would they be to a layperson?
    — How severe do they appear?
— For ongoing care of chronic conditions, the control of the disease, especially compared to expectations relative to prescribed treatment when followed as planned.
— The child's development as compared to age.

Laboratory assessment
If there was delay in the caregiver seeking treatment, some laboratory tests may give information on diagnostic possibilities.

NUTRITIONAL NEGLECT (AT TIMES CALLED FAILURE TO THRIVE [FTT])

History
Focus on multiple key issues:
— Child's dietary intake, preferences, and growth pattern over time
— General health and well-being, beginning with both and continuing through the present
— Any known food intolerances or allergies
— Presence of vomiting, diarrhea, discomfort after eating, or rashes from specific foods
— Recent illnesses since the last visit
— Family dietary practices and food preparation processes
— Family's ability to obtain appropriate foods for the child
— Previous medical workups and results of previous interventions
— Caregiver concern   *(continued)*

Table 5-1. *(continued)*

Nutritional Neglect (at times called failure to thrive [FTT])

Physical examination
Accurate measurements of growth parameters and trends over time are essential, as is a "head-to-toe" physical examination focusing on any findings suggesting a disease or disorder that could explain the lack of growth.

Laboratory assessment
The laboratory assessment in the FTT workup is focused and directed by the history and physical examination. Large-scale laboratory evaluations are rarely useful and tend to identify only what would have been indicated in a more focused assessment.

Caregiver-child interaction
In the FTT evaluation, the investigators give special attention to how the caregiver provides food and responds to the child's cues: How much care is observable?

Physical/Supervisory/Safety-Related Neglect

History
Any indication of environmental hazards, including:
— Presence of poisons within the child's reach
— Failure to adequately childproof the house in which the child lives
— Failure to install and use smoke detectors
— Failure to appropriately use child restraints in motor vehicles
— Failure to use bicycle helmets
— Presence of unsecured firearms in the household
— Presence of illicit drugs in the household
Additionally, the healthcare provider may use potential screening questions to identify the following situations that could present a risk:
— *Hygiene.* Frequency of bathing, laundering, and toilet behaviors.
— *Clothing.* Types of clothing available, resources to acquire the clothing, selection of seasonal clothing; for example, if the child is in summer clothing and without a coat during midwinter, then a nurse must explore who made the decision and whether a winter coat is available.
— *Shelter.* Housing and its state of repair; safety of electrical, heating, and cooking conditions.
— *Custody/supervision.* Who besides the caregiver watches the child?

Physical examination
Note the general appearance of the child, including cleanliness, infestations with parasites such as scabies or head lice, and appropriateness of dress for the climate and weather conditions. Also look for evidence of acute or healed injuries, and check records to determine the history that the caregiver provided for each. If clothing is inappropriate for the climate, the provider should look for any evidence of environmental exposure, eg, frostbite on the fingers or toes.

Laboratory assessment
Order laboratory assessments according to diagnostic considerations suggested by the clinical information.

Caregiver-child interaction
Does the caregiver respond to the child's natural curiosity about the environment in a supportive manner while simultaneoulsy redirecting the child to safer activities? For example, if the child touches the electrical outlet, does the caregiver redirect him or her to a more appropriate activity? If the child climbs on a chair, does the caregiver move into a position to offer assistance and protection, or does he or she appear to ignore the child?

developmental level, the type of neglect, its severity, and the time period over which it occurred.[4] The consequences can be acute, short-term, or long-term and can involve both physical and psychological functioning. For example, there is a clear association between infant malnutrition and persistent deficits in growth. Malnutrition also weakens the immune function and puts children at risk for a variety of infectious diseases. Medical neglect can lead to poor health and well-being. Preventable injuries may be experienced if appropriate attention is not paid to a child's safety, including reasonable "childproofing" of the environment.

The neurological and psychological consequences of child neglect are difficult to define clearly, as there are few long-term studies that adequately control for all the factors necessary for well-designed research. However, numerous adverse neurological, psychological, and school performance–related outcomes have been associated with child neglect, including impaired problem-solving abilities, academic underachievement, depression or withdrawal, behavioral problems, and poor peer relations. In addition, some adult survivors of child neglect have subsequently experienced alcoholism, drug abuse, criminal convictions, and premature death. Some children are able to rise beyond poor care and show remarkable resilience to the effects of child neglect when moved to a stimulating, supportive environment. Providing additional food sources and healthy emotional support may result in improved behavior, better peer relations, and improved problem-solving skills. Positive long-term outcomes can be promoted with earlier delivery of developmental stimulation and nutritional assistance.

Neglect also has societal effects, especially when one considers the impact it has on child health and well-being, and the social programs that are created in response to these effects. Further societal impacts are seen in law enforcement, the courts, and the juvenile and adult criminal justice systems. The overall impact of neglect on a child's life is immeasurable, and its financial costs are estimated to be in the billions of dollars each year when all the various hidden expenses are added up.[13,14]

INTERVENTIONS

Child Neglect: A Guide for Intervention provides a comprehensive discussion of a variety of issues related to child neglect, including guidelines for assessing and intervening in cases of child neglect.[15] Assessments and interventions are tailored to the type of neglect being considered and are shaped by the information gathered during assessment. These guidelines state that a person who observes a case of neglect and wishes to intervene should[16]:

— Assume that parents want to improve the quality of care for their children.

— Identify and reinforce hidden strengths of families and build interventions upon them.

— Be culturally sensitive.

— Avoid grouping families; instead, see each family as unique.

— Build parent's feelings of self-esteem, hope, and self-sufficiency, and avoid fostering dependency in children.

— Clearly outline service plans and use case management to manage formal and informal services.

— Set clearly-stated, limited, achievable goals; work to gain agreement and understanding by parents and children; reinforce the parents' incremental steps.

— Use legal action to protect children as a last resort.

Most interventions incorporate a risk assessment tool that systematically looks at a number of factors related to the family, its structure, and its previous involvement with CPS. The presence of any factors on the list indicates that the children may be at risk for neglect. The contents of each list vary but typically include a combination of the following 9 factors[15]:

— A single, isolated caregiver in the home at the time of referral

— Caregiver history of drug or alcohol abuse

— Age of youngest caregiver at the time of referral

— Number of children in the home

— Previous referrals for neglect

— Number of previous out-of-home placements

— Whether the caregiver was neglected as a child

— Whether the caregiver is involved in primarily negative social relationships

— Motivation for change on the part of the caregiver

Age-appropriate interventions for a child at risk are designed based on the information pulled from the assessment. For families who are neglecting their children but are found to be capable of providing adequate care, a program of supervision and involvement helps them meet the children's basic needs. Children's cognitive abilities, social development, and emotional well-being are prioritized along with the obvious medical and physical well-being issues. Often, these families are supported and encouraged to enroll their children in programs and services within the community that offer developmental stimulation, encourage curiosity, and promote exploration and learning in a safe environment. These "therapeutic" programs consist of focus areas tailored to preschool-aged, school-aged, and teenaged children. Referred to broadly as *therapeutic childcare*, they support child development for particularly vulnerable children and adolescents. **Table 5-2** describes the essential characteristics for preschool-aged children.

As children grow and mature, their developmental and physical needs change, and therapeutic childcare programs need to focus more on preventing school failure or dropout, decreasing delinquent behavior, and avoiding other dysfunctional behaviors. **Table 5-3** lists the programmatic modifications for therapeutic childcare directed at school-aged children and adolescents in need.

Table 5-2. Essential Characteristics of Therapeutic Childcare for Preschoolers

Physical Environment
— Safe and comfortable environment to enhance the emotional and physical growth of the children
— Large indoor space for movement, with specific areas for quiet play, active play, reduced stimulation, retreat, behavioral problems, and counseling or therapy
— Enclosed outdoor area for children to play in
— Variety of toys and materials that are stimulating, age-appropriate, and stored in areas accessible to the children
— Safe food preparation area
— Door-to-door transportation provided for children and for field trips

(continued)

Table 5-2. *(continued)*

Staff

— Low child-to-staff ratio, traditionally 2 to 6 children per 1 staff member; lower ratio for very young or more disruptive children; higher ratio for children aged 2 years and older
— Low enrollment in each setting: if childcare provider is in his or her own home, 4 to 6 children; for a group setting with multiple caregivers, 8 to 10 children
— Knowledge of and ability to apply child development theory
— Good observational skills, including the ability to observe and assess childrens' deficits and strengths
— Flexibility
— Ability to model good parenting to parents
— Ability to model appropriate behavior to children
— Acceptance and understanding of parents
— Awareness of community systems and resources
— Training in a variety of disciplines; for example, child development, arts, special education, and developmental psychology
— Diversity, in terms of sex, race, and age
— Presence of a staff support group
— Ongoing, in-service staff training
— Paid psychologist or psychiatrist for consultation

Program Design

— Clear admission criteria and intake procedures
— Multidisciplinary consultation team for evaluation, treatment planning, and progress assessment input
— Individualized treatment program written and updated for each child, with ongoing supervision and consultation
— Structured day program for children with a routine curriculum and schedule, typically 4 to 5 days per week and 4 to 6 hours per day
— Play therapy
— Provision of high-quality nutrition for children (and parents) during program attendance
— Infant intervention for children younger than 18 months who are too young for structured therapeutic childcare but need stimulation and supervised parent-child play interaction
— Parent participation in the program, addressing both parents' and children's needs by providing supervised parent-child interaction and home visits, the purposes of which include observation of the parents, modeling parenting skills to them, establishing a therapeutic relationship with them, training them in child development and their child's special needs, and providing services for them, including recreational activities and individual or group counseling or therapy
— Separate staff serving and advocating for children and parents
— An established understanding community support network including medical, legal, and protective services
— Planning for, recommendation of, and referral to after-care services
— Follow-up inquiries on families, particularly on the children's development, after they have left the program

Data from Gaudin.[15]

Table 5-3. Programmatic Modifications Necessary for School-Aged Children and Adolescents

Supports in School
— Special education programs with low child-to-teacher ratios, structured learning-by-doing activities, positive reinforcement, and the best computer-assisted learning technology available to help remedy deficits in cognitive stimulation and motivation to learn
— Tutorial programs using professional teachers or volunteers to provide neglected children and adolescents with necessary academic help and encouragement and a relationship with a nurturing adult to help overcome academic deficits

Counseling Supports
— Group counseling and personal skills development classes to provide opportunities for developing life skills appropriate to age and developmental level; especially appropriate with younger maltreated children because their observations and interpretations of commonly shared experiences exert a corrective influence on one another
— Volunteer Big Brothers and Big Sisters to provide neglected children with emotional nurturing, tutoring, cultural enrichment, recreation activities, and positive role modeling as well as vocational and career counseling

Parent Supports
— Volunteer or paid paraprofessional parent aide programs to provide one-on-one assistance to parents through childcare activities and provide supplemental parenting to children while parents are learning to improve their childcare abilities

Data from Gaudin.[15]

If assessments indicate a family will be unable to provide a safe and developmentally healthy environment, if the neglect is severe, or if the neglect is unlikely to be remedied by available interventions, then CPS pursues a plan that will either temporarily or permanently remove children from their original home. Such arrangements are referred to as *foster care* when the new caregivers are unrelated to the child and as *kinship care* when they are related. CPS considers removing children from their family a major disruption and takes this action very seriously. If necessary, a temporary placement may later be converted to permanent removal. In this case, the court terminates the parent's /parents' parental rights once appropriate legal processes occur. As serious as out-of-home placement is, leaving children in an unsafe or developmentally deficient environment is even more harmful to their overall well-being. **Table 5-4** lists the situations that CPS considers when pursuing out-of-home placement.

CONCLUSION

Child neglect is a distinct form of child maltreatment. It differs from physical and sexual abuse in its origins, manner of revelation, potential impact on children, and required interventions. Because neglect rests at the root of having one's basic needs met or not met, the potential negative impacts are both physically and emotionally significant. By paying attention to a child's appearance and well-being, as well as to the quality of the caregiver-child interaction with a focus on how responsive and comforting the caregiver is, and by pursing specific issues related to an identified basic need when general concerns are raised, we can help children whose needs are not being met by neglectful caregivers.

Table 5-4. Out-of-Home Placement Considerations

Imminent danger to physical health
Is the child seriously ill or in imminent danger of serious illness or injury? Children who are abandoned, suffering from malnutrition, suffering from serious physical illness, or in an extremely dangerous living situation should be noted. Young children who must depend on mothers addicted to drugs or alcohol are at risk for serious, life-threatening injury or illness

Age
Infants and toddlers are the most vulnerable to serious harm. Most child fatalities from abuse and neglect occur in children younger than 3 years.

Disability
Children with mental or physical disabilities are more vulnerable to serious injury.

History of previous child abuse or neglect
Is the neglect chronic or due to recent stressful life events? Are there previous reports of child abuse and/or neglect? Have there been prior placements outside the home? Chronic neglect and prior out-of-home placements are indicators of greater risk.

Parent's motivation and capacity to improve adequacy of child care
Does the parent acknowledge severely inadequate care? Does the parent's behavior indicate minimal willingness to improve the level of care? Does the parent have the mental and physical ability to provide minimally adequate care? Does the parent have a serious alcohol or drug problem?

Data from Gaudin.[15]

REFERENCES

1. Hobbs CJ, Hanks HGI, Wynne JM. Failure to thrive. In: Hobbs CJ, Hanks HGI, Wynne JM, eds. *Child Abuse and Neglect: A Clinician's Handbook.* New York, NY: Churchill Livingstone; 1993:25-28.

2. Zuravin SJ. Child neglect: a review of definitions and measurement research. In: Dubowtiz H, ed. *Neglected Children: Research, Practice, and Policy.* Thousand Oaks, Calif: Sage Publications; 1999:24-46.

3. US Department of Health & Human Services, Administration on Children, Youth and Families. *Child Maltreatment 2004.* Washington, DC: US Government Printing Office; 2006. Available at: http://www.acf.hhs.gov/programs/cb/pubs/cm04/index. htm. Accessed July 3, 2006.

4. Gaudin JM Jr. Child neglect: short-term and long-term outcomes. In: Dubowitz H, ed. *Neglected Children: Research, Practice, and Policy.* Thousand Oaks, Calif: Sage Publications; 1999:89-108.

5. Dubowitz H, Black M, Starr RH, Suravin S. A conceptual definition of child neglect. *Crim Justice Behav.* 1993;20:8-26.

6. Garbarino J, Crouter A. Defining the community context for parent–child relations: the correlates of child maltreatment. *Child Dev.* 1978;69:604-615.

7. Garbarino J, Sherman D. High-risk neighborhoods and high-risk families: the human ecology of child maltreatment. *Child Dev.* 1980;51:188-198.

8. Burke J, Chandy J, Dannerbeck A, Watt JW. The parental environment cluster model of child neglect: an integrative conceptual model. *Child Welfare*. 1998;77: 389-405.

9. Dubowitz H, Giardino AP, Gustavson E. Child neglect: guidance for pediatricians. *Pediatr Rev*. 2000;21:111-116.

10. Paschall R. The chemically abused child. In: Giardino AP, Alexander R, eds. *Child Maltreatment: A Clinical Guide and Reference*. St. Louis, Mo: GW Medical Publishing; 2005:113-152.

11. Prevent Child Abuse America. *Recognizing Child Abuse: What Parents Should Know*. Prevent Child Abuse America Web site. September 2003. Available at: http://www. preventchildabuse.org/publications/parents/downloads/recognizing_abuse.pdf. Accessed July 3, 2006.

12. Crouch JL, Milner JS. Effects of child neglect on children. *Crim Justice Behav*. 1993;20:49-65.

13. Daro D. *Confronting Child Abuse: Research for Effective Program Design*. New York, NY: The Free Press; 1988.

14. National Clearinghouse on Child Abuse & Neglect Information. *Prevention Pays: The Costs of Not Preventing Child Abuse and Neglect*. Washington, DC: National Clearinghouse on Child Abuse & Neglect Information; 1998:1-5.

15. Gaudin JM Jr. Child Neglect: *A Guide for Intervention*. Washington, DC: US Dept of Health & Human Services; 1993. User Manual Series. Contract No HHS-105-89-1730.

16. National Clearinghouse on Child Abuse & Neglect Information. *In Focus: Acts of Omission: An Overview of Child Neglect*. Washington, DC: US Dept of Health & Human Services; 2001.

Chapter 6

DATING VIOLENCE

Eileen R. Giardino, RN, PhD, CRNP
Angelo P. Giardino, MD, PhD, MPH, FAAP

Parents and caregivers of high school– and college-aged adolescents are becoming increasingly concerned about the possibility of dating violence, both threatened and actual. However, there are still many parents who are uninformed on the topic, or even completely unaware of it, despite its relatively common occurrence. Education is paramount for encouraging adults and adolescents to talk about this very real and serious problem. Although dating violence may occur in any period of life,[1] this chapter will focus on adolescence.

DEFINITIONS

Dating violence is a type of abusive behavior that occurs between people who are dating, whether they already have or may have an intimate relationship. Violence may begin at any point of the dating process: at first meeting, during the dating relationship, and even after the relationship has ended. Dating violence can take place in heterosexual and same-sex relationships. Generally, the term "dating violence" does not apply to people who are living together.

Dating violence has many forms. One may experience a single incident of violence, such as "date rape" or sexual assault, or a repeated pattern of abusive behavior that escalates over time. Perpetrators tend to try to exert power and control over their victims by using threatening behavior or physical, sexual, or psychological violence. Other forms of abusive behavior in dating situations include emotional victimization, threats, isolation from friends and family, control over what someone wears or with whom a person socializes, insults, and name-calling.[1]

SIZE OF THE PROBLEM

Statistics show that dating violence is widespread. According to one survey, approximately 9% of high school students have experienced physical dating violence.[2] Perpetrators can be male or female, but the US Department of Justice estimates that 85% of dating violence victims are female and that most perpetrators are male.[3] Although female adolescents and adult women make up the overwhelming majority of victims, the percentage of male victims may actually be higher than calculated because abuse professionals believe that male victims underreport their own victimization.

An opinion survey of parents revealed that 81% either believe that teenaged dating violence is not an issue or are unsure if it is an issue. In addition, 54% of those surveyed reported they had not spoken to their child about dating violence.[4] The spectrum of abusive dating behaviors ranges from shoving, pushing, and hitting (12% to 35% of teenagers) to more serious physical harm (18% of high school girls and 7% of high school boys).[5] According to a December 1995 Children Now/Kaiser Permanente poll, 40% of high school girls report knowing someone who has been beaten or hit by a boyfriend.[6] Some figures indicate that 20% of female high school students have experienced physical and/or sexual violence by a dating partner,[7] while forced sex has been experienced by 8% of high school girls.[5] **Table 6-1** shows some statistics that are significant for types of violence that occur among teenagers and young adults.

Table 6-1. Statistics of Teenaged Dating Violence
— About one third of high school students have been or will be involved in an abusive relationship.
— 40% of girls aged 14 to 17 years say they know someone their age who has been hit or beaten by a boyfriend.
— 20% of dating couples report some type of violence in their relationship.
— 20% of college females will experience some form of dating violence.
— One study found that 38% of date rape victims were girls aged 14 to 17 years.
— A survey of adolescent and college students revealed that date rape accounted for 67% of sexual assaults.
— 68% of young women raped knew their rapist either as a boyfriend, friend, or casual acquaintance.
— Women aged 16 to 24 years experience the highest per capita rates of intimate violence—nearly 20 per 1000 women.
Data from Rennison and Welchans.[3]

TYPES OF DATING VIOLENCE

Dating violence can involve physical, sexual, or psychological violence. The following descriptions of victimization provide examples of types of interactions and abusive acts that may occur in a dating relationship.[1,8]

PHYSICAL VIOLENCE

Physical violence involves the use of force that may or may not result in physical injury or involve the use of a weapon. It often manifests as a pattern of behaviors that are abusive and harmful. Behaviors seen in physical dating violence include the following[1]:

— Restraining

— Shaking

— Pushing or shoving

— Throwing something hard

— Kicking

— Hitting or slapping

— Hair-pulling

— Biting

— Choking

— Burning or scalding

— Beating

Sexual Violence

Sexual violence is a term that includes all forms of sexual harassment, sexual coercion, or sexual assault. Sexual harassment is a pattern of unwelcome or unwanted sexual words, behaviors, or actions. Sexual coercion involves manipulating a situation or person unfairly in order to get sex. Sexual assault includes any form of sexual activity without gaining the partner's consent. Behaviors seen in these 3 forms of dating violence are listed in **Table 6-2**.

Table 6-2. Types of Behaviors Seen in Sexual Dating Violence

Sexual Harassment
Behaviors, actions, or words that are all of the following:
— Sexual in nature
— Likely to offend or humiliate
— Repeated even after the person has been told to stop

Sexual Coercion/Violence
— Pressure to engage in sexual acts by taunting, belittling, making fun of, or harassing
— Lying to someone or threatening to tell lies about someone (eg, to damage their reputation) in order to get sex
— Exploiting or taking sexual advantage of someone, including someone younger or intoxicated, and including using the Internet or date rape drugs to prey on someone for sex

Sexual Assault
— Any form of kissing, fondling, touching, oral sex, or sexual intercourse without consent
— Forcing someone to engage in sexual intercourse or any other sexual act
— Not stopping sexual contact when asked

Data from Department of Justice of Canada.[1]

Psychological Violence

Psychological violence involves using words or actions to intimidate, isolate, or control someone. The abuser's intent is to damage the victim's sense of integrity or self-worth. Psychological dating violence includes[1]:

— Cruelty, deceit, or manipulation

— Ridiculing, name-calling, or insulting

— Constant criticism

— Excessive jealousness and possessiveness

— Attempts to control whom the person is friends with, talks to, or spends time with

— Threats toward the partner, their loved ones, or their property if they do not obey

— Stalking or harassing behaviors after a relationship has ended, such as obsessive phone calls or making threats

— Bullying behaviors such as swearing, name calling, vandalizing property, or spreading gossip or rumors about the person

INTERVENTIONS AND SUPPORT

Dating violence is often hidden from parents and other caregivers because teenagers are usually not experienced in intimate relationships. They may think that such intimidating behavior is an acceptable or expected part of dating (**Table 6-3**). The way in which teenagers view themselves may also influence whether they accept or perpetrate dating violence.

Table 6-3. Problematic Male and Female Beliefs About Dating Roles

Young men may be erroneously socialized to believe that:
— They have the right to control their female partners in any way necessary.
— Masculinity involves physical aggressiveness.
— They possess their partner.
— They should demand intimacy.
— They may lose respect if they are attentive to and supportive of their girlfriends.

Young women may be erroneously socialized to believe that:
— They are responsible for solving problems in their relationships.
— A boyfriend's jealousy, possessiveness, and physical violence is romantic.
— Violence is "normal" because their friends are also being victimized.
— There is no one to ask for help.

Data from In the Know Zone.[9]

Teenagers can be encouraged to actively choose better relationships when they, with the support of those who care about them, learn to identify the early warning signs of an abusive relationship, understand that choices exist, and have reason to believe that they are valuable individuals who deserve to be treated with respect. Signs that a teenager or college student is now or may in the future be experiencing violence or victimization in a relationship are listed in **Table 6-4**.

Parents, teachers, and other caregivers need to stress that no one ever deserves to be victimized or threatened. We must also recognize that it is difficult for abusers to change their ways. In fact, violence in a relationship usually gets worse over time, not better. Talking to a trusted person, preferably an adult, about the problem can help youths in abusive relationships. It may be necessary to locate an agency or support group within the community that serves victims of domestic and dating violence. With the aid of another person, it is possible for victims to plan what can and should be done to end the relationship while still remaining safe.

According to the Domestic Violence Advocacy Program of Family Resources, when teenagers go out on dates with new or unfamiliar people, parents and other caregivers should encourage them to follow these guidelines[10]:

— Consider double-dating the first few times you go out with a new person.

— Before leaving on a date, know the exact plans for the evening and make sure a parent or friend knows these plans and what time to expect you home. Let your date know that you are expected to call or tell that person when you get in.

— Be aware of your decreased ability to react under the influence of alcohol or drugs.

Table 6-4. Identifying Dating Violence in Teenagers

Identifying a potential victim	A person who is being victimized may: — Stop participating in things he or she enjoys. — Have little or no interest in family activities. — Have difficulty sleeping. — Be unable to concentrate. — Experience memory problems. — Start missing school more often. — Experience a drop in his or her grades. Some of the signs that a person is being victimized include: — Low self-esteem. — Withdrawal. — Depression. — Nervousness. — Unexplained cuts, bruises, scrapes, burns, or bite marks.
Identifying a potential perpetrator	A person who is being abusive may: — Get too serious too quickly. — Feel he or she needs to make all the decisions. — Manipulate and control the other person's contact with friends, family, and outside activities, or isolate them from friends and family. — Put down the other person's ideas, friends, family, and appearance. — Impose excessively limiting, rigid, and stereotypical views of male and female relationships. — Threaten others. — Blame others. — Use guilt as tool of manipulation ("If you love me . . ."). — Make accusations of dishonesty. — Make obsessive phone calls and constantly check up on the other person. — Follow and watch the other person (stalking). — Demand to know the other person's whereabouts at all times. — Refuse to take "no" for an answer (which may include refusing to accept breaking up). Some of the signs that a person is being abusive in a relationship include: — Low self-esteem or poor self-image. — Low tolerance for frustration. — Mood swings. — A short temper (tending to express fear or anxiety as anger, or refusing to discuss feelings and then blowing up in explosive anger). — Extreme jealousy. — Overpossessiveness. Other indications that a person may become abusive include that they: — Brag about bullying or harming others. — Drive too fast or engage in other dangerous behavior. — Use alcohol and/or drugs (and then becoming angry or violent). — Are cruel to animals.

Adapted from Department of Justice Canada.[1]

— If you leave a party with someone you do not know well, make sure you tell another person you are leaving and with whom. Ask a friend to call and make sure you arrived home safely.

— Assert yourself when necessary. Be firm and straightforward in your relationships.

— Trust your instincts. If a situation makes you uncomfortable, try to be calm and think of a way to remove yourself from it.

It is important for teenagers and young adults to think about ways to be safe in a dangerous or potentially dangerous relationship. It is ideal for caregivers to discuss issues of dating violence and safety with their teenagers along with other important topics. That way, if a difficult or concerning situation arises, teenagers will already know that someone is ready to listen and help.

Victims of dating violence should strongly consider performing the following actions:

— Change their school locker or lock.

— Change their route to and from school.

— Use a buddy system for going to school, classes, and after-school activities.

— Keep a journal describing the violence.

— Get rid of or change the number to any beepers, pagers, or cell phones.

— Keep spare change, calling cards, the number of the local shelter, the number of someone who could help them, and restraining orders (if applicable) with them at all times.

In addition, there are several questions that victims should plan answers to:

— What adults can you tell about the violence and victimization to help you stay safe?

— What people at school can you tell—teachers, principal, counselors, security?

— What friends can you tell?

— If stranded, who could you call for a ride home?

— Where could you go quickly to get away from an abusive person?

— What other things can you do?

STUDENT PROTECTION ON COLLEGE CAMPUSES

In 1990, Congress enacted a law requiring schools of higher education to track and report crimes that occur on and around campuses. The law was first titled the Student Right to Know and Campus Security Act (CSA). A 1992 amendment to the law required schools to afford sexual assault victims on campus certain basic rights. The CSA was renamed the Jeanne Clery Disclosure of Campus Security Policy and Campus Crime Statistics Act (or the Clery Act) in 1998, in memory of a Lehigh University student who was raped and murdered in a residence hall.[11] When Jeanne Clery's family learned that their daughter's university had not told students about 38 violent crimes that had occurred on campus in the previous 3 years, they joined with families of other campus victims to ensure that schools of higher education publicly disclosed crimes on campus. In 1998, reporting requirements of crimes were expanded, and in 2000, another amendment was passed requiring schools to notify the campus community about where they can obtain public information on registered sex offenders on campus.

Although the Clery Act does not oversee the actual security measures offered by a college campus, it does require that the school publicly report information about crime incidents. In turn, students, parents, and caregivers are more aware of crime and hopefully more in tune with what should be done to prevent it. Schools must disclose campus statistics for crimes that occur in unobstructed public areas on or around the campus, including certain noncampus facilities as Greek housing and remote classrooms. The Clery Act requires the following crimes be reported to the campus community:

— Homicide

— Sex offenses

— Robbery

— Aggravated assault

— Burglary

— Motor vehicle theft

— Arson

Statistics must be gathered from campus police or security, local law enforcement, and other school officials who have significant responsibility for student and campus activities such as student judicial affairs directors. In order to protect confidentiality and encourage victims to seek help, professional mental health and religious counselors are exempt from reporting obligations but may refer patients to a confidential reporting system.

CONCLUSION

Dating violence has emerged as a serious and pervasive problem facing high school– and college-aged adolescents and young adults. Even though teenagers and young adults are maturing, they can still benefit from having concerned parents and caregivers helping them understand that violence and intimidation are unacceptable in intimate relationships. By becoming aware of the early warning indicators of potential dating violence and being supportive listeners, parents and caregivers can help end this problem. The extent of the problem is only now coming to light, and caregivers and other adults need to increase their efforts to communicate clearly to teenagers and young adults that dating violence is not acceptable and must stop.

REFERENCES

1. Department of Justice of Canada. *Dating Violence: A Fact Sheet from the Department of Justice Canada*. July 21, 2005. Available at: http://canada.justice.gc.ca/en/ps/fm/datingfs.html. Accessed July 17, 2006.

2. Centers for Disease Control & Prevention. Physical dating violence among high school students: United States, 2003. *MMWR Morb Mortal Wkly Rep*. 2006;55: 532-535.

3. Rennison CM, Welchan S. *Bureau of Justice Statistics Special Report: Intimate Partner Violence*. Washington, DC: US Dept of Justice; May 2000. Available at: http://www.ojp.usdoj.gov/bjs/pub/pdf/ipv.pdf. Accessed May 2, 2006. NCJ 178247.

4. Charron P, Cappello D, Wiseman R. *A Parent's Guide to Teen Dating Violence: 10 Questions to Start the Conversation*. New York, NY: Liz Claiborne; 2001. Available at: http://www.loveisnotabuse.com/pdf/10questions_hand.pdf. Accessed August 22, 2006.

5. The Commonwealth Fund. *The Commonwealth Fund Survey of the Health of Adolescent Girls*. New York, NY: The Commonwealth Fund; November 1997.

6. Domestic violence is a serious, widespread social problem in America: the facts. Family Violence Prevention Fund Web site. Available at: http://www.endabuse.org/resources/facts. Accessed August 22, 2006.

7. Silverman JG, Raj A, Mucci LA, Hathaway JE. Dating violence against adolescent girls and associated substance use, unhealthy weight control, sexual risk behavior, pregnancy, and suicidality. *JAMA*. 2001;286:572-579.

8. Lavoie F, Robitaille L, Hébert M. Teen dating relationships and aggression: an exploratory study. *Violence Against Women*. 2000;6:6-36.

9. Dating violence: why do abusers abuse. In the Know Zone Web site. 2005. Available at: http://www.intheknowzone.com/dating_violence/abusers.html. Accessed July 14, 2006.

10. Dating violence. Alabama Coalition Against Domestic Violence Web site. Available at: http://www.acadv.org/dating.html. Accessed August 22, 2006.

11. Jeanne Clery Disclosure of Campus Security Policy and Campus Crime Statistics Act, 20 USC § 1092(f) (1998).

Chapter 7

SCHOOLS AND CHILD ABUSE

Peggy S. Pearl, EdD
Angelo P. Giardino, MD, PhD, MPH, FAAP

Schools have legal and ethical reasons to be involved in cases of child abuse and neglect. Teachers and school personnel can report an abuse or neglect case, be involved in its investigation, or even be alleged perpetrators. Teachers are often in a difficult position in relation to child abuse issues, but they are legally required to be involved as reporters and ethically obligated to participate in community efforts to improve the well-being of all children. Teachers and other school professionals take the legal responsibility to report suspected acts of child abuse or neglect very seriously and consistently make a large percentage of child abuse and neglect reports: In 2004, 16.5% of all reports were made by school personnel.[1]

TEACHERS AND SCHOOLS AS MANDATED REPORTERS

Teachers in all 50 states, US territories, and the District of Columbia are mandated by law to immediately report all suspected cases of child abuse or neglect to a state child protective services (CPS) agency. Thus, school teachers are referred to as *mandated reporters*. The law does not require individuals who make such reports to prove that the abuse actually occurred, as that will be determined in the investigation that follows. The reporter has immunity from civil liability and criminal penalty as long as they reported in *good faith*. This term means that the individual believed at the time of the report that abuse truly occurred and made the report without malice or specific intent to harm. The reporter understood the indicators of child abuse, observed those indicators, and/or was told by the child of possible abuse or neglect.

CONTENTS OF REPORTS

Teachers and school personnel making a report of suspected child abuse and neglect typically are asked to provide the following information:

— Name of the child

— Age of the child

— Home address or address where the child can be located

— Parent(s) name, phone number, and address, if known

— Type of abuse

— Alleged perpetrator (Some states will ask, but most of the time the reporter will not know the perpetrator and should not make unfounded allegations. If the child told the reporter, then this information should be included as part of the report.)

— Specific indicators of the abuse and neglect (What exactly led the reporter to make the report?)

— Whether this is an emergency and the child is in imminent danger

— Name, phone number, and address of the reporter (Some states allow anonymous reports, but knowing the name and phone number allows the state agency to obtain additional information if necessary.)

SCHOOL POLICIES ON REPORTING

School districts must have clear and specific written policies for reporting child abuse and neglect. These policies give school personnel, including teachers, nurses, counselors, social workers, and administrators, guidance regarding what specific steps to take and how to fulfill the state statute. The school district protocol supports teachers and reduces feelings of vulnerability. Standardized policy also prevents some children's needs from being ignored, some parents from being the victims of prejudice, and some personnel from becoming overzealous. Policies typically address all forms of child abuse and neglect, including alleged abuse by school district personnel. After reporting a case to a CPS agency, reporters have specific procedures to follow. Some states automatically provide follow-up information to a reporter, while in other states the reporter needs to inquire about how the case gets resolved. In still other states, reporters do not even have access to that information, due to confidentiality requirements between CPS and public schools.[2]

Teacher education programs in colleges and universities should include specific information on the identification of child maltreatment and other forms of violence and victimization.[3] For teachers already working in public or private schools, in-service training should include education on the legal requirements of reporting child abuse and neglect as well as specific indicators of all types of maltreatment. Workshops should address mandated reporting responsibility, the possible indicators of child abuse and neglect, and how to appropriately document observations.[4] Good documentation of behavioral, physical, and educational indicators makes reporting easier.

PENALTY FOR NOT REPORTING

Nearly every state penalizes mandated reporters for failing to report child abuse or neglect. The penalty ranges from a misdemeanor to a felony charge. Some states convict mandated reporters whether the failure to report was deliberate or accidental, and regardless of whether they even knew a report was required in the first place. In addition to repercussive action from the state, a failure to report can also result in an individual or school district being sued in civil court. Civil action will not result in imprisonment of the negligent staff member, but it can result in a financial award to the individual filing the case. Because of this, individuals and school districts alike work diligently to follow state laws, district policy, and their own moral obligations when deciding whether to make a report of child abuse and neglect.

AFTER SUSPECTED ABUSE OR NEGLECT IS REPORTED

Once a report has been made to the state child abuse and neglect hotline, school personnel are expected to be supportive of the child. Disclosed child abuse, especially sexual abuse, becomes a crisis for both the child and family involved. In order to support the child, staff and faculty members should:

— Treat the child in the same way before and after the report. Many times, a child is pitied or treated as if he or she has been "broken" or "damaged."

— Treat the child with respect and understanding; be sensitive to the child's needs.

— Be sensitive to times when the child may need to talk.

— Be sensitive to times when the child may need to be alone.

— Be aware of mood changes. Children often feel depressed or anxious after a report, and these feelings, especially when sexual abuse is involved, can lead the child to retract the story. If this happens, do not assume that the abuse did not occur.

— Help a sexual abuse victim avoid inappropriately touching others by defining appropriate behaviors.

— Listen when the child appears to want to talk; do not quiz. Observe and respond to nonverbal communication.

— Praise the child for his or her courage in reporting, and assure the child that it was not his or her fault.

— Do not promise the child that the abuse will never happen again (since that cannot be guaranteed).

— Provide the child with opportunities to feel in control of self and the environment.

WHAT IF THE ALLEGATION IS DISPROVEN AFTER INVESTIGATION?

After an allegation is made and an investigation is carried out, the charge may be determined to be false. False allegations do occur, and they come from various sources. Sometimes, a false accusation is made by the child. It can be that they have misinterpreted the situation, or that the content of their accusation has been misinterpreted by another, though these instances are rare. Another possibility is that the child willfully made a false accusation, something that can occur at any age. Children who make intentional misrepresentations are typically emotionally disturbed, seeking attention, coached by someone else, or, in very rare circumstances, seeking revenge. Determining the reason that a false report was made can often be helpful for both the child and the alleged perpetrator, since both will be in need of support in the aftermath of the investigation.[5]

WHEN ABUSE INVOLVES A SCHOOL EMPLOYEE

School district policies include special procedures to follow when a school employee is the alleged perpetrator of child abuse. If the individual has direct responsibility for children, the school district must determine whether the employee can safely continue in his or her role. Several questions must be considered during the investigation, and the rights of the accused individual must be balanced with the priority of ensuring the safety of children in the school. The questions include the following[5]:

— Will the employee be moved to another position that does not have contact with children?

— Will the employee be placed on paid or unpaid leave?

— Will there be a change in the supervision of the employee?

— Will the employee retain access to children?

Most investigations take about 30 days, sometimes longer. When the individual's position does not require direct contact with children, immediately removing the employee from the position during the investigation may not be warranted. Examples of such positions include school district office personnel, financial officers, and maintenance staff.

When a report is made, the principal or other school administrator should attempt to gather facts rather than defend the staff member or school system. As with any case of suspected child abuse and neglect, the interview of the child should be conducted by CPS and/or law enforcement investigators to avoid placing excessive hardship on the child. State law varies slightly as to what agency investigates cases of abuse and neglect outside of the child's home—CPS, the juvenile court, or law enforcement officials. Depending on the situation, the school system may be named as the alleged perpetrator.

When a parent comes to the school to report an abusive employee, the principal should listen carefully and take notes on what is said. He or she should maintain an open attitude and listen without accusing staff members, becoming defensive, or denying accusations. During the discussion, the principal should inform the parent that making a report to the state child abuse and neglect hotline is the next appropriate action. The school must keep a record of the entire discussion. In most instances, individuals named in allegations should not be told of the allegation until an investigative worker interviews them. The school administrator should then meet with the employee to hear his or her version of what happened. Next, the administrator should meet with any other people the child or the alleged perpetrator names in order to gather related information.

Children with special needs are at high risk for abuse from all child caregivers, including teachers. Selecting qualified teachers to work with these children is especially important. The in-service training of individuals who work with children with special needs should include the particular areas they, as the children's caregivers, are likely to have to deal with, for example, personal hygiene, discipline, and restraint. The teacher working with a team of professionals must regularly re-evaluate the developmental appropriateness of all classroom procedures and practices.

DISCIPLINE IN SCHOOLS

Although schools still use corporal punishment in some states, school districts are increasingly moving away from it and, in fact, are starting to institute policies that explicitly prohibit it.[6] The use of corporal punishment is discouraged because it may be associated with the following effects[6-8]:

— Negative influence on learning

— Increased aggressive behavior in children

— Increased fearfulness and anxiety in children

— Failure to encourage children to learn self-discipline

Teachers, disciplinarians, and principals would likely benefit from being taught alternative methods of discipline and positive guidance techniques. Schools can then serve as role models for nonviolent conflict resolution for this and future generations of parents.[6,9]

All schools should have a written policy outlining appropriate disciplinary techniques that have been approved by parents, teachers, and other school personnel, and the policy should be provided to parents when they enroll their children. These policies should establish clear rules and expectations of students and provide projected nonviolent consequences for failure to comply with these rules. **Table 7-1** includes a list of items that should be included in the written disciplinary policies of all well-informed schools that have moved away from corporal punishment and towards more positive approaches to consistent discipline.

Some schools require that parents read and sign the disciplinary policy, indicating that they understand it. Other districts allow parents to exercise other options if they disagree with the stated policy. For example, in districts that permit corporal punishment, individual schools may give parents the ability to opt out of its use. Typically, parents need only to present a signed statement indicating that they do not want corporal punishment to be used with their child, and the school will honor their decision.

Table 7-1. Information That Should Be Included in School Discipline Policies

A statement of the program's philosophy regarding the guidance of children's behavior should include:
— The goal of discipline, which is to help children learn self-control.
— Discipline techniques that reflect realistic expectations for children's behavior based on an understanding of child development.
— Positive guidance techniques that are individualized, according to the situation and the child's age and stage of development.
— The prohibition of corporal punishment and isolation of children.
— The protection of children from verbal outbursts or remarks that are belittling or intimidating.
— Discipline approaches that will help children to develop problem-solving skills and learn the logical consequences of behavior.
— Examples of positive guidance techniques appropriate for children of different ages.
— A designation of who will discipline children and under what conditions.
— A designated point at which parents will be asked to participate in planning strategies to help children overcome troublesome behaviors.
— Methods for staff to assess the effectiveness of the discipline techniques being used.

Examples of instituted policies that reduce the need for punishment:
— Provide students with choices and options for decision making.
— Make sure students know the school's expectations and the consequences for noncompliance.
— Provide predictable routines in attractive, orderly, and effective classrooms.
— Increase positive interactions with adults inside and outside the classroom.
— Ensure developmentally appropriate curriculum.
— Provide opportunities to assist others in meaningful ways.
— Ensure that there are opportunities for students to feel pride in themselves in a cultural context.
— Encourage all school personnel to be alert and observant of individual students and the total environment to ensure appropriateness of these policies.

DEFENSE AGAINST ABUSE IN SCHOOL

The best defenses against abuse and false allegations of maltreatment are education, supervision, and open communication. School personnel should be regularly educated on what is and is not a developmentally appropriate environment for children of various ages. Additionally, educating children about "good touch" and "bad touch" helps them understand the appropriate adult-child relationships and their rights in inappropriate situations.

Supervising school personnel can be another important prevention technique. Are all personnel appropriately qualified for their position? Do they have adequate in-service training and supervision? Do they have opportunities to discuss situations with a supportive individual before situations become crises? Do personnel have opportunities to provide and receive peer support? Are all treated with respect, given opportunities to make appropriate professional decisions, and valued as contributing members of the educational team?

Staff and faculty members need opportunities to collaborate with peers. The collaborative effort will allow sharing of expertise and building on strengths to improve professional practice. Employees who support each other will be better able to support and respect the strengths of the children and families they work with.

Schools should practice openness as much as possible. Openness means that parents are encouraged to participate in the school and that there are few, if any, places in the building where staff can be alone with children. Window shades or curtains are either removed or readily movable, except when needed for specific purposes.[10] Openness also means that children are only alone in a room or office with an adult when there is a specific reason, such as individual testing or counseling. When arranging for adult supervision of elementary school restrooms, schools need to ensure that supervision plans do not permit individual adults to be routinely alone with only 1 or 2 children, since that may create an unsafe, isolated environment that might permit abuse to occur.

Even when pursuing openness, there are some instances when access to the school should be controlled. Schools should routinely require individuals who are not staff or faculty to sign in and out of the office so that the administration is aware of who is in the building. The goal of a routine sign-in policy is not to deter parents from entry, but rather to provide them with the security of knowing that efforts are being made to keep their children safe.

BEYOND THE LEGAL MINIMUMS

Because of their special relationship with children and families, schools must work with the entire community to support families. As an African proverb states, "It takes a village to raise a child." Schools should send representatives to serve on community-based child protection teams, participate in local community councils on child abuse prevention, and initiate the formation of such groups if they do not exist. Schools should be leaders in developing a wide range of community prevention programs and treatment services. **Table 7-2** identifies some of the ways schools can support families. All parents should have access to parenting information and support services. Collaborative work with human services agencies, CPS, the juvenile court, and law enforcement will assist educators in staying current on topics related to child welfare in the broader sense.[11] The interaction will also facilitate an exchange of concerns and improve communication to build a better community for everyone.

Because schools play a central role in the social world of children and families, they should consider themselves morally bound to offer prevention programs to facilitate the positive development of parenting skills in this and future generations. **Table 7-3** identifies some specific long-range prevention programs that schools should consider. The curriculum should include instruction on nonviolent conflict resolution, interpersonal communication, child development, resource management, and stress management. Schools must respond to the cultural, economic, and social changes within each community to assist the children and families in coping with these changes. School professionals may then see themselves as morally and ethically bound to assist in the prevention of child abuse and neglect and intervention on behalf of abused children.[11,12]

Table 7-2. Ways Schools Can Support Families

— Provide accessible, affordable before-school and after-school childcare for working parents and help identify community resources with available programs for holidays and summer vacations.

— Provide parent education and support groups for parents with special concerns, including those who are divorcing, single, noncustodial, grandparents-as-primary-caregivers, foster parents, or parents of children with special needs.

— Provide parent education classes to help them learn age-appropriate expectations for their children.

— Provide evening, day, and/or Saturday parent-teacher conferences for custodial and noncustodial working parents.

— Implement family play nights to allow parents free or inexpensive opportunities to enjoy parenting more and to relieve routine life stresses. Open playgrounds to families on evenings and weekends.

— Institute homework help lines to allow students and/or parents to obtain assistance with homework.

— Incorporate more parents into the school volunteer program. This builds the self-esteem of both children and parents.

— Offer within the schools Alcoholics Anonymous (AA) and Narcotics Anonymous groups for parents and students, as well as Al-Anon for the friends and families of alcoholics.

— Allow community groups the use of school facilities for family or child art, drama, music, recreation, and sports groups during evenings and on weekends.

Table 7-3. Long-Range Child Maltreatment Prevention Programs

— Teach nonviolent conflict resolution skills beginning in early childhood classrooms and use peer playground monitors.

— Involve parents and children in policy development.

— Involve parents in lunchroom, library, and playground supervision.

— Include a wellness curriculum that addresses both physical and emotional wellness for all grades.

— Provide support groups to students experiencing similar life stresses, such as divorce, death of a family member or friend, family or community violence, substance abuse in the family, relocation, or peer problems.

— Initiate volunteer programs that encourage each student to use his or her skills to help others in the community.

— Provide work and play experiences for each child with individuals who are different from him or her.

— Allow all children opportunities to achieve their dreams.

According to one estimate, approximately 1 out of every 7 children in US schools has experienced some type of child abuse.[13] Of the approximately 41 million children in America's elementary and secondary school classrooms, nearly 6 million are victims of child abuse and neglect.[13] These statistics represent more than mere, impersonal numbers. Because the actions of adults in caregiving roles can damage a child's potential, these numbers must be thought of as children and families, not just interesting statistics.

Because maltreated children have predictable classroom behaviors, developmental abilities, and academic needs, teachers can play a pivotal role in providing a positive environment that can enhance children's maturational process. The remainder of this chapter briefly describes students with a history of abuse and neglect and discusses some teaching techniques that may optimize the classroom environment for abused and maltreated children.

CHARACTERISTICS OF CHILDREN WITH A HISTORY OF ABUSE OR NEGLECT

Different types of abuse are associated with a wide range of effects, including preoccupation, depression, sudden changes in behavior, modesty, sexual acting out, and suicidal tendencies. Although the presence of these characteristics does not prove that children have been maltreated, it should prompt one to ask whether it is possible and likely under existing circumstances. The duration of the abuse, the age of the child at the time, and the relationship of the abuser to the child all shape the effects of the abuse and how they manifest in the victim. More problematic behaviors develop as the child matures, but no single, specific finding is consistently observed in all cases of child abuse and neglect.[14,15]

In learning to survive in their environment, child abuse victims generally adapt in 1 of 2 ways: (1) with externalized and uncontrolled behaviors, such as aggression, or (2) with internalized and overcontrolled behaviors, such as social withdrawal and depression. The stereotype of child abuse victims is aggressive, negative children who are incapable of playing or working acceptably with other children or adults. However, this description only accurately covers a portion of the victims. If that image is in the forefront of most adults' minds, it is because aggressive and hyperactive children demand the most attention and are the ones adults are forced to deal with. Their symptoms are often similar: They appear to be impervious to disapproval, and they attack other children both physically and verbally. Their impulsivity, distractibility, and inability to delay gratification prevents any relief from their demands on teacher attention. They may see themselves as bad, unlovable, and/or stupid. They expect punishment and will call attention to their own misbehavior, appearing to gain little or no pleasure from activities or people. Without treatment, these children only become more aggressive. However, they can respond well to a very calm, highly structured environment.

As suggested above, the aggressive description only covers a portion of child abuse victims; the remaining portion behaves in an almost opposite way. This segment of the population is highly compliant and may appear to accept whatever happens to them. They are passive and obedient, withdrawn and shy, and easy to overlook. All of these behaviors are survival techniques. Abused children sometimes feel guilty for misbehaving and responsible for upsetting their caregivers or getting their caregivers in trouble. They are very sensitive to criticism from adults and require only mild suggestions to redirect their behavior. They need an environment that is accepting and encouraging. These children will respond best in calm, predictable surroundings that allow them to learn social skills and release their feelings. Often compulsively neat and overly desirous of meeting adult goals, they feel little joy or pleasure and have low self-esteem but may show indiscriminate affection for adults.

STRATEGIES FOR TEACHERS

Teachers need to make each classroom developmentally appropriate, using their understanding of their students' differences in developmental abilities, personality traits, learning styles, and family backgrounds.[16] The teaching strategies below are most effective with victims of abuse and neglect but are appropriate for all children. Topics and techniques are divided into separate sections for ease of discussion only; in the developmentally appropriate classroom, they are integrated.

BUILDING A SENSE OF TRUST

Children learn to trust themselves, and therefore others, when caring adults meet their needs predictably. When children are maltreated at home, where this basic trust normally develops, it frequently fails to grow. Trust can be learned later in life, however, when adults act in consistent, caring ways. The structure and routine of the classroom, for example, provide predictability and facilitate the development of trust. Teachers also help children develop a sense of trust when they keep their promises. By observing teachers plan, implement, and evaluate routine activities, children gain confidence that adults are capable of meeting their needs. Teachers should call all children by name, listen to what they say both verbally and nonverbally, anticipate their needs, and then respond. Children who know that someone is listening begin to feel safe. To keep children's trust, teachers must maintain confidentiality and be someone children can always count on.

Adolescents who were abused at an early age and lack a basic sense of trust find this stage of life to be an especially difficult one. From a developmental psychology perspective, the adolescent is asking all adults, "Can I trust you to do what you say you will? Do your actions agree with my ideal concept of what should be?"[17] Because maltreatment victims come from families where roles are often indistinct, they can be uncertain about what is "normal" and need to learn what is appropriate and positive. Without a basic sense of trust, adolescent victims cannot rely on adults and, therefore, have difficulty sorting out what they believe and value. To improve their sense of trust in themselves and others, these teenagers need to be surrounded by adults who are consistent and dependable. Teachers need to respect privacy, protect confidentiality to the extent permissible by the situation, and routinely model respectful interactions with the students.[15]

EXPECTING SUCCESS

As simple as it sounds, one of the most effective ways to build success is to expect success. Children who feel that others care about how well they do are more likely to achieve. To build success in children, teachers must say they care about each child and illustrate it through their actions. Many abused children, especially those who have been neglected, have never known what it is to have others support their efforts and direct them toward achievement. Maltreated children commonly suffer from intellectual delays as a result of abuse, neglect, or their general home environment. Even when a home provides materials and opportunities for intellectual development, stress and anxiety impede the normal acquisition and use of knowledge. However, their homes more often lack age-appropriate learning opportunities, guidance, and reinforcement of learning. Children who have been abused may initially lack the motivation and joy for the learning experienced by normal children. In an environment in which they are accepted as they are, allowed to succeed, and encouraged to meet their own needs rather than the needs of adults, these children eventually experience the joy of learning and develop curiosity.[18] The classroom must provide an environment in which children can learn intellectual skills when they are emotionally ready.

Students should be placed in learning situations in which they are assessed according to their work. Academic performance should be evaluated as an issue separate from the student by comparing a student's work to a predetermined standard of performance. Teachers should evaluate products, not the producers. "Not all of the math problems are correct" is an objective statement about the student's work that does not reflect on the student as a person. However, the statement, "You failed to work all of your math problems correctly" does make a personal attack on the student and will likely leave them feeling devalued. When teachers require students to evaluate their own work against a predetermined evaluation scale, they create an environment that enhances students' feelings of control and may allow them to feel successful and self-determining.[19] This type of instruction, referred to as "programmed instruction," also empowers students to monitor their own progress rather than require the teacher to do so exclusively. Along the same vein, teachers should also provide a wide variety of opportunities for children to construct their own ideas. Children, regardless of background, need multiple opportunities to improve their knowledge base. Different learning styles and emotional states influence the acquisition of knowledge. Students need a learning environment structured to build successes rather than correct failures.

TEACHING SOCIAL SKILLS

Positive social skills allow children who have been abused and neglected to reduce their isolation and build a web of relationships. These children have an even greater need than most to feel connected to others in a mutually supportive system. Abusive families can be isolating, untrusting, and fearful of the outside world, and the children of such families may have no positive role models except those they see at school. Feelings of connectedness help build bonds of trust while reducing fear—another example of the interrelatedness of human development.

Teachers should encourage abused children to stand up for themselves and should support them when they do. Initially, an aggressor may listen only because the teacher is literally standing behind the victim, but emphasizing the notion that people have rights and should assert them appropriately and effectively is important. Children whose personal rights have been violated need a safe haven and someone to model nonviolent ways to prevent further violation. Teachers should make efforts to help them develop assertiveness and resistance and provide opportunities for them to interact with a small group of peers. The adult working with this small group must defend and support each individual's rights while directly teaching skills that will assist each group member in successful group interaction. Mainstreaming a maltreated child into a group of children who have not been maltreated allows the victimized child to see models of appropriate behavior. A child's ability to learn social skills is directly related to his or her successful emotional development.[18,20]

TEACHING LIFE SKILLS

The curricular content of all classrooms should allow students to learn life skills such as health and physical education, money management, stress management, nonviolent conflict resolution, nutritional competence, food preparation, and interpersonal communication in a setting free of racial, ethnic, or gender bias. Teachers should set realistic standards, not ideals, because students who have lived in dysfunctional homes may already have difficulty distinguishing between "what is" and "what should be." Students need to learn that all families have money management problems and that planning is the best way to prevent the problem. Older students in math, business, and home economics classes can practice resource management, communication, and negotiation skills by having classroom exercises based on case studies of individuals and families solving money management issues. By practicing problem-solving and decision-making skills in the classroom, students experience an alternative family lifestyle. Simple group projects in any discipline allow them to construct knowledge relating to the subject matter as well as learn interpersonal communication and negotiation skills. Students should be allowed to make age-appropriate decisions and live with the consequences, for example, "Would you rather work with Erin or Sandy?" or "Which of these 3 books would you like to read for Monday?" All of the choices must be real and require students to accept the consequences of their decisions. All classroom activities must reflect various socioeconomic levels and cultural and ethnic backgrounds. Self-esteem develops in the context of mastering changing life tasks and challenges.

TEACHING COMMUNICATION SKILLS

In most abusive homes, interpersonal communication is poor.[21] School curricula should include units on interpersonal communication, conflict resolution, and family/personal resource management. These units are especially important to young people who have no role model for appropriate interpersonal communication. In abusive families, the person in whom ultimate power is vested may communicate in vague terms or expect no 2-way communication. Children may have been routinely punished for replying to adults even conversationally; therefore, a curriculum must begin with the basics. Additionally, a classroom must be structured to give all students opportunities for communication with peers as well as with the teacher.

When giving instructions to a child, adults should make sure the directions are clear and simple. Teachers should use a clear, quiet voice, while looking directly at the child. Because children feel that what is nearer to them is more important, an adult should be physically near the child to whom he or she is giving directions. Children who have lived with many commands and general uneasiness will not respond well to general directions given from across the room. Teachers should be specific when instructing children, yet give some latitude to allow children to make simple decisions. It is also important that an adult's words and body language convey the same message. Child abuse victims are not easily fooled by people who say one thing and do another. Calm body language will placate and relax them more than words. Vocal tone is also more important than what is said, and teachers should be careful to make sure that their voice conveys what is intended. "Time to begin writing now?" (with an unsure tone) prompts children to challenge the spoken words, whereas, "It is time to begin writing," stated in a clear, calm manner, tells children what to do.

Adults should be specific when telling children what behaviors or actions are appropriate and expected. "Clean up your desk and get ready for lunch" is too vague. "Place the writing papers in your folder, put the folder in your desk, return all books to the shelf in alphabetical order, wash and dry your hands, and then go to the lunch table," however, provides children with clear directions. The more concise and specific the directions, the better they define appropriate actions. After children complete directions, teachers need to provide lots of praise and smiles. Teachers and other school personnel should model calm behavior and exhibit an appropriate sense of humor.[16,22,23] Calmness and humor keep children from feeling unnecessarily anxious about their behavior.

Puppets can be used to facilitate language development and communication skills. They provide opportunities for students at various developmental levels to gain new experiences. Young students may use them for storytelling, acting out stories, or free play. Middle school students may be involved in the preparation of puppet shows or simple presentations for younger students. Puppets may also provide an avenue for children who have been maltreated to release feelings and gain relief from disclosure. Puppets are versatile educational tools that facilitate development in many areas.

Allowing Students to Be Students

Victimized children may be overly helpful to teachers and classmates if they have been reared in an environment in which they cared for parents and younger siblings. These students may be the ones teachers love to have in class or the assistants they so desperately need; however, teachers must not succumb to the temptation to always accept help from students who seem to need to give and enjoy giving. Because these children have probably been praised and accepted only for doing responsible, helpful tasks, especially cleaning, they are using survival techniques that they know will earn them praise in school. As important as it is for children to learn helpfulness, they also need to develop skills in relating to peers as equals and adults as caregivers. When they lack academic and social skills, children try to succeed by helping. Although this behavior often gains approval—and perhaps passing grades—from the teacher because it is easy to reinforce, students may fail to learn appropriate communication or social skills and are often further victimized by peers.

Teaching Positive Coping Skills

Students need instruction in good management and coping skills, including various opportunities to practice those skills. Students with a history of abuse and neglect have often developed dysfunctional coping skills—ones that promote additional victimization, self-defeating behaviors, abuse, and neglect. Such children and adolescents frequently follow poor role models. The resulting behavior is either inappropriately acting out or becoming depressed. Because of the number of hours teachers spend with children each day, they are ideal role models for positive coping skills. It is possible to teach empathy, understanding the points of view of others, good verbal skills, attentiveness, reflectiveness, problem-solving skills, inner locus of control, tolerance of frustration, and appropriate responses to success. Some other behaviors are more complex and global and do not easily lend themselves to an instructional and training approach; it is less easy to teach children how to detach from the dysfunctional behaviors of others, be personable and well-liked, think creatively, practice autonomous thinking, be optimistic, have a sense of humor, be aware of personal power, orient themselves toward the future, and have a well-developed value system. Teachers can teach coping skills using modeling, role-playing from scripts, or by allowing students to view videos that set up a situation and then require the students to discuss the alternative solutions.

Another thing teachers should do is integrate resource management into the curriculum. Students can learn how to avoid many stressful situations using good management techniques. Resource and stress management programs are available in a variety of formats. Some interactive computer programs may be especially helpful for students who lack the language skills necessary for verbal role-playing.

Prevention programs are necessary for stopping bullying and assisting both the bully and the victim with learning more appropriate social skills. Abuse victims are frequently passive and lack the ability to stand up for themselves. As a result, they often become the targets of bullying behaviors and continue to be victimized by both adults and other children. Bullying behavior by peers further emotionally abuses the child and makes treatment much more complex and long-term. Assertiveness training will assist these children in standing up for themselves.

When someone in a child's family is an alcoholic, confrontation skills are essential to the child's positive coping strategies. However, teaching confrontation skills requires more involvement than a classroom teacher can provide, and these situations are best handled by referring children to community resources, including mental health professionals or support groups like Alateen, which offers support and guidance to young relatives of alcoholics (http://www.al-anon.alateen.org). Classroom teachers can offer support and educate students about the resources available to individuals and families with chemical addiction problems, but of course teachers are not therapists, so though they can be supportive, they do not treat the problem per se. Teachers should role model positive responses to stress and ensure that the classroom environment does not cause children additional stress.

PROVIDING PLEASANT EXPERIENCES

There is merit in making learning fun, or at least pleasant and enjoyable. Children who have been maltreated have had few, if any, experiences of pleasurable activities, and often when they do have fun, they are not allowed to appropriately enjoy it. The school is an important place for the student to develop new interests, hobbies, and skills. All students, but especially students who have been abused or neglected, need to hear teachers speak about the pleasant odors, flavors, and textures in the world around them. Students who have been abused or neglected often may not have had their senses stimulated in common and pleasant ways.[24] Physical education, art, music, science, and family and consumer sciences offer a wide variety of firsthand exploration of the world through the senses.[24] Teachers can help the students by continually looking for ways of adding pleasant sensory experiences to the curriculum.

BUILDING SELF-ESTEEM

Self-esteem is a complex, multifaceted phenomenon related to the development of values, moral character, and personality. It involves an individual's feelings about his or her social, cognitive, moral, and physical/motor abilities. The 4 major aspects of self-evaluation are acceptance, power/control, competence, and moral virtue.[15,20]

All teachers should be aware of the importance of student self-esteem and include in the curriculum ways for children to improve their self-images. These activities are especially important to children who have been victimized and have experienced extreme external control and manipulation. Exercises should encourage students to focus on their positive abilities and actions, to learn positive behaviors, and to seek methods for self-improvement. Fugitt[25] provides a variety of activities for building students' self-esteem and helping them progress from victim to survivor. Improving their knowledge of the world around them also provides students with information on community resources, such as opportunities in athletics, dance, physical education, art, and music, and how to access those resources for personal growth. For all students, knowledge brings with it feelings of power and control, which are essential to building positive self-esteem.[20]

Children's opinions about their uniqueness and individuality will also improve as they gain mastery over their bodies. Physical education, recreation, drama, and movement/dance can all provide valuable opportunities to gain greater body awareness, define personal boundaries, and improve self-image. Additionally, physical activities allow the individual to stimulate the senses, release feelings and anxiety, engage in communication, experience physical and emotional joy, and know feelings of control and freedom. When physical recreation is a group activity, it provides additional opportunities for developing decision-making, problem-solving, coping, and communication skills, as well as a sense of trust. Programs that involve survival training, such as Outward Bound, are especially helpful to participants in developing trust, cooperation, impulse control, self-confidence, and self-sufficiency. If properly structured, physical activities may also allow individuals to feel the joy of success.

In order to build their sense of worth, children need opportunities to be responsible, caring members of society. Acting as a student librarian, listening to younger students read, volunteering at a recycling center, or working as a stage hand for the school or community theater allows children to feel that they are capable of helping others. Teachers need to empower children to understand that they can choose to make a difference through public service. Choosing to care is different from perpetuating the role reversal and overly responsible behavior that may be necessary survival techniques in a maltreated child's home. When caring for others is a choice, service allows the caring individual to feel personal value.

IMPROVING ACADEMIC SKILLS

Because of prior experiences, victimized children often lack curiosity, resourcefulness, independence, initiative, responsibility, goal-directed behaviors, and other dispositions necessary for learning. One third of all abused and neglected children repeat at least one grade in elementary school.[5] Ideally, the school experience allows children to slowly develop these inclinations. Childhood abuse and neglect interrupts the normal growth of trust, autonomy, independence, and initiative; in short, it robs children of their childhood. They must go back and work through each of these psychosocial stages and construct the knowledge necessary for academic competency. Teachers must structure the classroom environment to allow children with varied backgrounds and dispositions to learn.

As already noted, abused children need a learning environment that is calm, structured, and predictable. An individual study area may assist some children in focusing on the academic tasks before them. The classroom environment may overly stimulate children who have spent much of their lives in chaos. Other children may have or develop learning disorders and need to be evaluated for special services. Teachers must adapt classroom or curriculum structure for success. Instructions may need to be written and clearly divided into simpler tasks to allow a child to complete parts of the total assignment and then move to the next one rather than feel overwhelmed by complex tasks. Children who have not lived in calm, ordered environments need special attention.

PROVIDING AVENUES TO GAIN INSIGHT

Reading books on relevant topics is one way for children who are the victims of abuse to gain personal insight. This directed reading may be called ***bibliotherapy***, which literally means "to treat through the reading of books." The goals of bibliotherapy are as follow[15]:

— Teach students to think constructively and positively.

— Encourage them to talk freely about their problems.

— Help them analyze their attitudes and modes of behavior.

— Point out that there is more than one solution to a problem.

— Stimulate an eagerness to find an adjustment to problems that will lessen conflict with society.

— Assist them in comparing their problems with those of others.

Although teachers are not therapists or counselors, they can request that school libraries make available books about children who have dealt positively in adverse circumstances, and these books can then become part of required and optional assignments (**Table 7-4**). High school students working as assistants in child development laboratories, elementary schools, or school or community libraries can also gain insight into their own lives by reading these books to younger children or acting them out with puppets. In addition to providing therapeutic opportunities for students who have been mal-treated, these books teach all students what appropriate treatment of children is and become part of a child abuse prevention program.[15]

Table 7-4. Examples of Books for Bibliotherapy
Alphin EM. *Counterfeit Son*. New York, NY: Harcourt Children's Books; 2000.
Carner T. *Puppet Child*. New York, NY: Pagefree Publishing; 2002.
Clifton L. *One of the Problems of Everett Anderson*. New York, NY: Henry Holt; 2001.
Deaton W, Johnson K. *My Own Thoughts and Feelings on Stopping the Hurt: A Child's Workbook About Exploring Hurt and Abuse*. New York, NY: Hunter House Publishing; 2002.
Deaton W, Johnson K. *No More Hurt: A Child's Workbook About Recovering From Abuse*. New York, NY: Hunter House Publishers; 2002.
Havelin K. *Incest: "Why am I Afraid to Tell?"* Mankato, Minn: Capstone Press; 2000.
Holmes MM, Mudlaff SJ, Pillo C. *A Terrible Thing Happened: A Story for Children Who Have Witnessed Violence and Trauma*. Washington, DC: Magination Press; 2000.
Hopkins BH. *My Mom Has a Bad Temper*. Washington, DC: Child & Family Press; 2001.
Kehoe P. *Something Happened and I'm Scared to Tell: A Book for Young Victims of Abuse*. New York, NY: Parenting Press; 1987.
Loftis C, Gallagher C. *The Words Hurt*. New York, NY: New Horizon Press; 1994.
Ottenweller J. *Please Tell!: A Child's Story About Sexual Abuse*. New York, NY: Hazelden; 1991.
Page CG. *Hallie's Secret*. Chicago, Ill: Moody Press; 1990.
Turner AW. *Learning to Swim: A Memoir*. New York, NY: Scholastic Signature; 2002.
Woodson J. *Our Gracie Aunt*. New York, NY: Jump At The Sun; 2002.

RESILIENCY OF CHILDREN

Many children have overcome the devastating effects of abuse and neglect and become successful in school and life. Researchers have described these children as invulnerable, stress resistant, or "vulnerable but invincible."[26] Regardless of the label assigned to them, these children typically share the following 4 characteristics:

1. An active, evocative approach to solving life's problems, enabling them to success-fully negotiate an abundance of emotionally hazardous experiences

2. A tendency to perceive their experiences constructively, even if the experiences caused them pain or suffering

3. The ability to gain other people's positive attention

4. A strong ability to use faith in order to maintain a positive vision of a meaningful life

Teachers can help children turn their vulnerability into resiliency through the following actions:

— Encouraging children to reach out to friends, teachers, and others

— Accepting the children and assisting them in building on their strengths, rather than expecting failure and allowing them to become overwhelmed with their problems

— Conveying to the children a sense of responsibility and caring and rewarding them for helpfulness and cooperation

— Encouraging the children to develop a special interest, hobby, or activity that can serve as a source of gratification and self-esteem

— Modeling coping skills

— Providing dependability

When someone cares enough to reach out to a maltreated child and provide him or her with an alternative to giving up, the child can overcome social and developmental obstacles that might otherwise become debilitating.[26]

CONCLUSION

In the United States, school teachers are one of the professional groups who are legally mandated to report suspicions of child maltreatment. They are not required to prove that abuse or neglect occurred, but only to inform authorities of the reasons they suspect it has occurred. School districts should therefore adopt policies and programs for preventing, identifying, and reporting abuse and neglect. In addition, they should provide all personnel and parents of children in the district with copies of the district policies on discipline and child abuse and neglect reporting.

Because child abuse and neglect can potentially have significant negative impacts on normal development, parents, caregivers, school personnel, and health professionals all need to think about how schools can help children after cases of maltreatment come to light. Without intervention, the negative impact of maltreatment may become increasingly serious. Children who have been maltreated typically perform poorly on academic tasks.

Although classroom teachers are not therapists, they can provide victimized students with insight and opportunities to facilitate personal growth through specific classroom assignments, and they can make referrals to other sources of assistance in the school system or community. Teachers and all school personnel can be important role models of predictability, trustworthiness, and joyful living and learning. In addition to legal policies, schools have ethical policies that support families in fostering the optimal development of each child. Being ready to learn requires many things, including freedom from intolerance, community and family violence, and prejudice. It does indeed take a village to raise a child, and schools can form a nurturing component of that caring village.

REFERENCES

1. US Dept of Health & Human Services, Children's Bureau. *Child Maltreatment 1996: Reports From the States to the National Child Abuse and Neglect Data System.* Washington, DC: US Government Printing Office; 1998. Available at: http://www.acf.hhs.gov/programs/cb/pubs/ncands96/index.htm. Accessed July 6, 2006.

2. Duncan N. When should teachers report abuse? *Children's Voice*. November/December 2001. Available at: http://www.cwla.org/articles/cv0111teachers.htm. Accessed July 6, 2006.

3. Hazler RJ, Miller DL, Carney JV, Green S. Adult recognition of school bullying situations. *Educ Res*. 2001;43:133-146.

4. Pence DM, Wilson CA. Reporting and investigating child sexual abuse. *Future Child*. 1994;4:70-93.

5. Tower CC. *The Role of Educators in the Protection and Treatment of Child Abuse and Neglect*. Washington, DC; US Department of Health and Human Services; 1992. DHHS Publication No. ACF 92-30172.

6. Hyman IA. *The Case Against Spanking: How to Discipline Your Child Without Hitting*. San Francisco, Calif: Jossey-Bass Publishers; 1997.

7. Straus MA. *Beating the Devil Out of Them: Corporal Punishment in American Families*. New York, NY: Lexington Books; 1994.

8. Wissow LS. *Child Advocacy for the Clinician: An Approach to Child Abuse and Neglect*. Baltimore, Md: Williams & Wilkins; 1990.

9. Lowenthal B, Paul H. *Abuse and Neglect: The Educator's Guide to the Identification and Prevention of Child Maltreatment*. Brookes Publishing, Baltimore, Md; 2001.

10. Anderson EM, Levine M. Concerns about allegations of child sexual abuse against teachers and the teaching environment. *Child Abuse Negl*. 1999;23:833-843.

11. Tutty LM. Child sexual abuse prevention programs: evaluating. *Who Do You Tell*. 1997;21(9):869-881.

12. Daro D. Prevention of child sexual abuse. *Future Child*. 1994;4:198-223.

13. US Dept of Health & Human Services. *Child Maltreatment 2004*. Washington, DC: US Dept of Health & Human Services; 2006. Available at: http://www.acf.hhs.gov/programs/cb/pubs/cm04/index.htm. Accessed July 6, 2006.

14. Kendall-Tackett K. Timing of academic difficulties for neglected and nonmaltreated males and females. *Child Abuse Negl*. 1997;21:885-887.

15. Pearl P. Working with child abuse victims. *Illinois Teacher*. 1990;34:70-74.

16. Bredekamp S, ed. *Developmentally Appropriate Practice in Early Childhood Programs Serving Children Birth Through 8*. Washington, DC: National Association for the Education of Young Children; 1987.

17. Erikson EH. *Identity: Youth and Crisis*. New York, NY: Norton; 1968.

18. Forten A, Chamberland C. Preventing the psychological maltreatment of children. *J Interpers Viol*. 1995;10:275-295.

19. de Charms R. *Enhancing Motivation in the Classroom*. New York, NY: Irvington; 1976.

20. Lawrence D. *Enhancing Self-Esteem in the Classroom*. London, England: Paul Chapman Publishing; 1987.

21. Miller-Perrin CL, Perrin RD. *Child Maltreatment: An Introduction*. Thousand Oaks, Calif: Sage Publications; 1999.

22. Honig AS. Compliance, control and discipline. *Young Children*. 1985;40:47-52.

23. Honig AS. Stress and coping with children. *Young Children*. 1986;41:47-59.

24. Helfer RE. *Childhood Comes First: A Crash Course in Childhood for Adults*. 3rd ed. East Lansing, Mich: Author; 1991.

25. Fugitt ED. *"He Hit Me Back First": Creative Visualization Activities for Parenting and Teaching*. Rolling Hills Estates, Calif: Jalmar Press; 1983.

26. Osofsky JD. The impact of violence on children. *The Future of Children*. 1999:9;33-49.

Chapter 8

CHILDCARE ISSUES

Peggy S. Pearl, EdD
Angelo P. Giardino, MD, PhD, MPH, FAAP

For a variety of reasons, parents and caregivers of young children commonly require assistance from alternative caregivers and childcare providers. Obviously, selecting a caregiver or childcare provider is very important, as it can have lifelong impacts on the child. However, the goal of this chapter is not to make parents feel overwhelmed by the importance and complexity of that decision; rather, it is to alleviate caregiver anxiety by providing a sound plan of action to help match the community's resources with the family's values and needs. Child abuse and neglect are uncommon in childcare settings, but a good plan is still needed to help ensure that potential abusers are not chosen as childcare providers. Ideally, the parent should select a childcare provider who can be trusted to provide safe, developmentally appropriate care to their child.

According to 2 national experts on the health and safety of children in childcare, Drs. Timothy Shope and Susan Aronson, about 66% of children younger than 6 years spend at least 10 hours per week in various forms of out-of-home childcare.[1] As children approach school age, the likelihood of families with working mothers using center-based programs increases at the following rate[1]:

— 22% of families with children younger than 3 years use center-based care.

— 46% of families with children older than 3 years but younger than 4 use center-based care.

— 70% of families with children aged 4 years and older use center-based care.

Table 8-1 summarizes the types of arrangements used by families for childcare.

Table 8-1. Types of Childcare Arrangements Used by Families		
TYPE OF ARRANGEMENT	CHILDREN YOUNGER THAN 3 YEARS OF AGE WHOSE MOTHERS ARE EMPLOYED (1997)	ALL CHILDREN 3 TO 5 YEARS OF AGE (1991)
Parent-only care	27%	23%
Care by a relative	27%	23%
Nonrelative care	17% family childcare home; 7% nanny	16%
Center	22%	60%

Reprinted with permission from Shope and Aronson.[1]

TYPES OF SETTINGS FOR CHILDCARE

According to the national project Child Care Aware, 4 kinds of full-time childcare are available[2]:

— Care provided by relatives, friends, and neighbors

— Licensed/registered family homes, which provide care in a family home other than that of the child

— Childcare centers

— In-home caregivers, such as nannies or au pairs

Table 8-2 describes these types of childcare. Ultimately, each of the 4 has positive and negative aspects, and parents must make their decision based on personal preferences, financial resources, community availability, logistics, specifics related to the child, and what setting or format might be best for the child. Most families do not choose an in-home caregiver because it is considerably more expensive and more difficult to find than the other types of childcare.

Table 8-2. Childcare Options		
TYPE	DESCRIPTION	BENEFITS OF OPTION
Care provided by relatives, friends, and neighbors	— Parents leave the child with a family member or friend, a method at times called "kith and kin" care. — This type of care is frequently not regulated, though some states may require basic training in health and safety issues.	Parents may view this as easier to arrange and as warmer and more loving. These caregivers are likely to share the parents' values and expectations. This type of care may be free or low cost; alternatively, it may be bartered in turn for services or other assistance.
Licensed/ registered family homes	— Registered family home childcare is a family-operated business; care occurs in the provider's own home. — Although states vary in how they regulate these businesses, many states require licensing if more than 4 children are cared for. Minimum health, safety, and nutrition regulations are typically applied to these providers as well. Some family childcare homes have an assistant caregiver during all or part of the day.	Parents often see this as offering a "home-like" setting that may make children feel more comfortable and secure. These arrangements may be seen as more flexible, less costly, and potentially closer to home. Often, these registered family home childcare options are found via a referral from someone who has used and been pleased with the services.

(continued)

Table 8-2. *(continued)*		

TYPE	DESCRIPTION	BENEFITS OF OPTION
Childcare centers	— Childcare centers provide care for groups of children in a facility specially designed for childcare. — The maximum number of children per group is determined by childcare licensing, which is typically based on the age of the child and expectation of how much care they will need. — Licensing sets minimal standards related to health, safety, and nutrition but does not by itself guarantee quality programming.	Parents may view larger groups, varied caregivers, and occasional state inspections as beneficial. Also, the institutional aspect of this kind of care may make it highly dependable and provide for more staffing, additional space, and adequate resources with regard to educational programming and developmentally appropriate toys and activities.
In-home caregivers	— Care is provided in the family's own home by a caregiver who can be either a "live in" or "live out" nanny, housekeeper, or babysitter. — Most states do not regulate this form of childcare, though some regulate nanny placement organizations.	This option, often the most expensive, may be selected because it is considered the most comfortable for children, the most flexible, and convenient for the family.

Data from Child Care Aware.[2]

CHILD ABUSE AND NEGLECT IN CHILDCARE SETTINGS

According to the US Department of Health and Human Services, children's safety is a significant concern among parents who use childcare.[3] Thus far, research indicates that fewer instances of child abuse and neglect occur in out-of-home childcare settings than in homes or residential facilities. When child abuse does occur, professional experience shows that it is most frequently physical abuse in the form of excessive discipline, typically as a response to prior conflict with the child. Of significant concern to child health professionals is that parental permission for corporal punishment may, at times, have encouraged the excessive discipline.[4]

MAKING THE DECISION

Selecting a childcare provider is an important decision for any family. Parents are, in many ways, the experts on their children, and they should not discount the importance of their knowledge toward making a selection. The following 4 steps will help ensure that a good decision is made for the child and family:

1. *Assessment.* Collect relevant information about childcare options.

2. *Comparison.* Compare different settings and program offerings.

3. *Decision making.* Make the actual decision and finalize that choice.

4. *Follow-up and ongoing involvement.* Make sure that the child is safe, developmentally challenged, and that the program is delivering what was promised.

Each of these steps is described in greater length below. Because out-of-home care is the most common choice, the following descriptions are geared primarily toward that option, while in-home and part-time childcare are discussed separately.

ASSESSMENT OF OUT-OF-HOME PROVIDERS

Once parents decide that childcare is required, their first step is to collect relevant information. This demands both time and effort from the parent and families but is necessary for making a good decision. One factor to consider is the consistency of the arrangements, which research has shown to be important to the development of children's security and readiness for school. According to the National Association for the Education of Young Children, children will also fare better emotionally, socially, and cognitively when childcare centers or family childcare homes demonstrate the following[5]:

— Sufficient staffing, meaning an appropriate number of adults for each child. Optimally, parents should look at centers with fewer children per caregiver, or higher staff-to-child ratios.

— Small group sizes.

— High levels of staff education and specialized training.

— Low staff turnover and stability among the administration of the care facility.

— Appropriate levels of staff compensation.

A number of valuable brochures and other resources exist that can provide parents with information at the beginning of the assessment process. **Table 8-3** contains a listing of brochures produced and offered by Child Care Aware in both English and Spanish that can be accessed on the Internet. The National Child Care Information Center

---

Table 8-3. Useful Child Care Aware Brochures Available on the Internet

THESE BROCHURES CAN BE ACCESSED AT HTTP://WWW.CHILDCAREAWARE.ORG/EN/TOOLS/PUBS.

General Decision Making
— Give Your Child Something That Will Last a Lifetime . . . Quality Child Care
— Five Steps to Choosing Safe and Healthy Child Care
— Child Care Resources and Referral (CCR&R) in Your Local Community

Special Circumstances
— Choosing Quality Child Care for a Child With Special Needs
— A Guide for Dads: Give Your Child an Early Lead in Life . . . Quality Child Care
— Finding Help Paying for Child Care

Developmental Issues
— Matching Your Infant's or Toddler's Style to the Right Child Care Setting
— Learning to Read & Write Begins at Birth

Related Issues
— All in the Family: Making Child Care Provided by Relatives Work for Your Family
— Selecting a Quality After-School Program for Your Child
— Five Steps to Choosing Summer Child Care
— Making the Transition From Child Care to Kindergarten: Working Together for Kindergarten Success

(NCCIC), a national clearinghouse that serves to connect parents, providers, policy-makers, researchers, and the public to early childhood care and education information, is another readily available resource for parents. The NCCIC offers a valuable 5-page downloadable pamphlet containing Web site links to organizations that offer useful information related to choosing a childcare provider.[6]

Research

Parents will need to use community support services to learn about the out-of-home childcare options in their community. Parents should talk about possible providers with family, friends, and coworkers. They should also access Child Care Resource and Referral (CCR&R) agencies, which have a complete listing of available childcare in the community and are a valuable resource. CCR&R agencies offer help over the phone, in person, and on the Internet. These agencies' databases include programs' names, locations, hours of operation, costs, ages of enrolled children, the number of slots available, and other services such as transportation to and from school. Available free or for a small fee, CCR&R agencies can also provide parents with a list of existing childcare options, information on state licensing requirements, and sources of financial aid. To find a local CCR&R agency, contact Child Care Aware. If a community does not have a CCR&R, check the business listings of the phone book, employers' human resources office, or the local childcare licensing office. Before looking at an office's listings, though, parents need to clarify their preference for a family childcare home or a childcare center.

Licensing

The licensing process for childcare providers requires a complete investigation of the childcare facility, including an inspection of the physical premises of the facility, a review of staff qualifications, and an inspection of other records that must be kept on file in the facility. When a provider fulfills licensing requirements, parents have assurance that the program meets minimum standards regarding nutrition, daily activities, and children's health and safety. Licensing agency staffs also provide consultation services to childcare providers in an effort to encourage and support quality childcare.

Be aware that states vary in the specific laws and regulations regarding childcare. The childcare licensing office will be listed in the telephone directory. Contact information is also available on the NCCIC Web site.[7] Additionally, the complete documents for all state childcare licensing regulations may be found on the Web site of the National Resource Center for Health and Safety in Child Care.[8]

The licensing of childcare providers is a state function that is often part of either the state's department of health or child protective services (CPS). Be sure to:

— Ask the local childcare licensing office for a list of licensed facilities.

— Obtain and read a copy of the licensing rules.

— Read the records of each program you are considering. The licensing records are open to the public and can be very informative to parents.

The licensing process provides safety assurance for consumers. Just as with restaurants, beauty shops, and hospitals, licensing here indicates that basic health and safety standards are met. Most states also require adequate, safe equipment and materials, a planned curriculum appropriate to the ages of the children in the facility, and in-service training for the staff. States also require a criminal record and CPS histories on staff of any type of abuse and violence toward others. The structural safety of the building, water quality and temperature, safety of heating and cooling systems, number of appropriate fire exits, and other features are checked by either the licensing staff or other trained professionals. Any food that is served must be prepared and stored under sanitary conditions and meet the US Department of Agriculture nutrition recommendations.

One thing to keep in mind is that a license does not measure every aspect of a program. Licensing only assures that *minimum* standards are met. To assess the actual *quality* of a program, one must look at its accreditation as well.

Accreditation

Accreditation is a "stamp of approval" designed to promote quality programs in both licensed childcare homes and childcare centers for young children, covering children from birth through the age of 13 years. Accreditation is a voluntary process that involves a fairly extensive review of a center's efforts to meet high standards in the area of childcare and gives recognition to childcare providers who meet certain indicators of quality. Programs that meet quality standards are accredited by one of several organizations. Following is a list of accreditation organizations and their Web sites, where lists of accredited childcare providers can be found:

— National Association for the Education of Young Children (http://www.naeyc.org/accreditation/default.asp)

— National Association for Family Child Care (http://www.nafcc.org/accred/accred.html)

— National Early Childhood Program Accreditation (http://www.necpa.net)

— National AfterSchool Association (formerly the National School-Age Care Alliance) (http://www.naaweb.org)

The decision to seek accreditation demonstrates a provider's desire to offer a quality program. The standards are developed by professionals in early childhood care and education. According to the National Association for the Education of Young Children, the standards for homes and centers evaluate practices in the following areas[9]:

— Health and safety of the environment

— Building self-esteem in each child

— Providing positive guidance

— Providing for positive interactions between children and adults

— Effective home and childcare program coordination

— Creative development

— Language development, including pre-reading and reading skills

— Physical and intellectual growth and development

— Social and emotional growth and development

— Formal staff education and specialized early childhood training

— Effective staff communication

— Effective management practices

When at a childcare facility, parents should look for its licensing and accreditation certificates, which should be prominently displayed.

COMPARISON

Once parents have collected relevant information about various childcare options and providers, the second step in the decision-making process is to compare programs as they relate to the list of expectations, which will develop throughout the research process. Program comparison requires the parents' personal involvement in visiting the various programs.

Program Visits

It is usually best for parents to call and verify the information they have about all programs under consideration. When talking to the program director or care provider, parents should ask if they may visit at any time or if they need an appointment. If parents have the freedom to choose, they may want to plan to visit a prospective program at different times of the day, during different types of activities. When visiting, parents should note whether they feel welcome and are encouraged to come back.

Ask Questions

Tables 8-4 and **8-5** list some of the questions parents should ask themselves and features they should look for during the decision-making process. These checklists are designed to help them decide which features of childcare arrangements are most important to them and make sure that the arrangement they choose offers the features they believe are important. Note that not everything will apply to every family's situation. During the visit, parents should mentally ask and answer the following questions:

— How does the center or home look? Sound? Smell? Feel?

— What is the noise level? Excessive noise is a sign of lack of planning, and it can be a source of stress and distraction to both adults and children. Is there a pleasant hum of activity, or is there silence dominated by a teacher's voice? Is there uncontrolled noise?

— Are children busy learning as they play?

— Is the environment free of clutter and confusion, without being "too" clean and orderly? Do children make free choices between a variety of planned learning centers?

— How does the playground look? Feel?

Table 8-4. Questions to Ask When Choosing a Childcare Provider

Does the provider…
— Appear to be warm and friendly?
— Appear clean and neat, with good hygiene?
— Seem calm and gentle?
— Have an appropriate sense of humor?
— Seem to be someone with whom you can develop a relaxed, sharing relationship?
— Seem to be someone your child will enjoy being with?
— Feel good about himself or herself and his or her job?

(continued)

Table 8-4. *(continued)*

Does the provider...
— Have child-rearing attitudes and methods similar to your own?
— Consistently use positive language in stating expectations or when guiding behaviors, rather than saying "no" and "stop that"?
— Never threaten, shame, or ridicule when correcting a child's behavior?
— Treat each child as a special person?
— Understand what children can and want to do at different stages of development?
— Have the right materials and equipment on hand to help children learn and grow mentally and physically?
— Patiently help children solve their own problems?
— Provide activities that encourage children to think and talk things through?
— Encourage good health habits, such as washing hands throughout the day?
— Provide appropriate outdoor experiences each day, except in very harsh weather?
— Talk to the children and encourage them to express themselves through words?
— Encourage children to express themselves in creative ways?
— Have art, movement, and music activities suited to the ages of all children in his or her care?
— Seem to have enough time to supervise all the children in his or her care?
— Help each child to know, accept, and feel good about himself or herself?
— Help each child become independent in ways of which you approve?
— Help your child learn to get along with and to respect other people, regardless of their appearance, background, and behaviors?
— Accept and respect your family's cultural values?
— Provide a routine and rules the children can understand and follow?
— Take time to discuss your child with you regularly?
— Allow children to do things for themselves because they understand everyone learns from mistakes?
— Help children increase their vocabulary by talking with them, listening, reading aloud, and answering questions?
— Accept and respect all children, regardless of ability or special needs?
— Have previous experience and education in working with children in a group setting?

If you have a young child (newborn through the age of 4 years), does the provider...
— Seem to enjoy cuddling with your child?
— Spend time holding, playing with, and talking to each child?
— Look children in the eye when feeding, diapering, and talking to them?
— Provide stimulation by pointing out things to look at, touch, and listen to?
— Cooperate with your efforts to toilet train your toddler?
— Realize that toddlers want to do things for themselves and help children learn to feed and dress themselves, go to the bathroom, and pick up their own toys?
— Help children learn language by talking with them, naming things, reading aloud, describing what they are doing, and responding to their words?

If you have a school-aged child (aged 5 to 14 years), does the provider...
— Give supervision and security, but also understand the growing need for independence?
— Set reasonable and consistent limits?
— Allow each child to make choices and gradually take responsibility?
— Teach nonviolent conflict resolution techniques for children to use with peers?
— Understand school-aged child development?

(continued)

Table 8-4. *(continued)*

If you have a school-aged child (aged 5 to 14 years), does the provider...
— Help each child follow through on projects, complete homework, and find interesting things to do?
— Encourage literacy skills with writing, reading, public speaking, and dramatic activities?
— Listen to problems and experiences?
— Respect children when they express new ideas, values, or opinions?
— Cooperate with parents to set clear limits and expectations about behaviors?
— Understand the conflict and confusion older school-aged children feel about sex, identity, and pressure to conform?
— Provide your child with a good adult role model?

Table 8-5. Features Childcare Centers or Homes Should Have

— An up-to-date childcare license
— A current accreditation by the National Association for the Education of Young Children
— Enough space indoors (approximately 35 square feet/child) and outdoors (approximately 75 square feet/child) so all the children can move freely and safely
— Knowledgeable staff educated in child growth and development and in techniques for working with children in a group setting
— Low adult-child ratios and small group sizes
    — Newborn to 2 years: 1 adult to 4 children, no more than 8
    — 2 to 3 year olds: 1 adult to 8 children, no more than 16
    — 4 to 6 year olds: 1 adult to 12 children, no more than 24
    — School-aged children: 1 adult to 16 children, no more than 32
— Low staff turnover and high administrative stability
— An open environment where no adult is ever totally alone with a child and out of sight of other adults
— Parent handbooks to outline services provided, facility policies, procedures for ill children, and what is expected of the parents
— Written discipline policy distributed to all parents and known and followed by all staff members
— A discipline policy forbidding corporal punishment
— Written policy for the transfer of responsibility for children from parent to staff at the beginning of the day and from staff to parent at the end of the day
— Written policy on who may pick each child up from the center or home
— Regular rest periods for staff, away from children
— Written accident reports on file
— Written procedures for dealing with suspected abuse of children by staff
— Emphasis on managing the environment, not on managing the children

Observe
Parents should observe whether each program actively tries to provide the features and services it offers. For example, ask what the program goals are for the children. Does the answer match your goals for your child? Is it possible to see, during the visit, attempts to attain these goals? Ask how the program individualizes the curriculum so everybody learns. Listen for open-ended situations that encourage children to choose between 2 or 3 activities, ask questions, and explore interesting topics. Children should not all be

expected to do the same activities at the same time, except during mealtime and naptime.

Parents should also ask how program personnel define reading and writing for preschoolers. Listen for a broad, inclusive answer, such as, "Pretending to read a book or scribbling 'letters' are important pre-reading and -writing activities for preschoolers." Such broad answers are important since they indicate a flexible, developmentally optimistic approach to working with children and an approach that sees children as active learners and creative beings in their own right. Listening to and asking questions about what someone reads to them encourages children to read and write. School-aged children should be encouraged to read as well as write their own books.

Additional Considerations

Notes taken during visits to several childcare centers or family childcare homes will help parents make a final decision. Along with all the information they have collected, parents need to consider the following questions:

— How much can you afford to pay?

— During what hours is care available, and how is care provided after hours when parents arrive late to pick up their child?

— Where is the care located in relation to the parents' home and workplace?

— Where will your child be the safest and healthiest?

— Who do you feel will give your child the best care?

— Which caregiver offers the activities that your child will enjoy the most and derive the greatest benefit from?

Decision Making

The information parents have gathered, their knowledge of their child or children, their personal values and child-rearing experiences, and their personal judgments of people will all factor into their final decision. Once the selection is made and the enrollment is confirmed, there is still more to do. Parents should ask the childcare program for a written agreement that includes the following information:

— When the services will begin

— Starting and ending times

— Cost

— Agreement on how to handle unexpected delays in picking children up and what will be done in case of illness

— Emergency situation guidelines (protocols, phone numbers, parent preferences)

— Daily routines

— Discipline guidelines (parents are encouraged not to agree to corporal punishment, as combining overly-stressed or tired caregivers with corporal punishment can create the possibility for physical abuse)

— Responsibilities of the childcare provider

— Responsibilities of the parents

Most programs have a parent handbook, and some have a legal contract that both the parent and the childcare provider will sign.

Follow-up and Ongoing Involvement

Parents will need to continuously observe the childcare provider's interaction with them and the child, the environment at the home or center, and the child's reaction to being dropped off and picked up. When observing the childcare providers, parents should check to see that they routinely ask the children about activities and new friends. Parents should also listen attentively as children respond, noting any particular changes, especially abrupt ones. Also, pay close attention to the language that childcare providers use with and about children—ridicules, threats, and shaming should never be used with children of any age.

Parents should continue to drop by the childcare center or family childcare home at different times of the day. Parental presence will make the child feel good, and parents can gain reassurance that they made a good childcare decision. They should be suspicious if the center has rules limiting when they can visit their child or where in the facility they may go. Some programs share a list of parents' addresses and phone numbers, though many cannot due to confidentially policies. Getting to know the parents of other children enrolled in the program allows parents to share observations. If a parent group exists, participating in that activity may also be helpful in making sure that the program goals are actually being implemented.

Only give permission for planned field trips and sign releases for individual outings, not a blanket approval for all field trips. Also make sure that appropriate transportation is provided, such as buses or vans with safety seats and drivers with the appropriate licenses. Of course, this does not mean that providers cannot, for example, decide to take children for a walk around the block to look at the leaves. Parents choosing a family home provider should find out when children will be routinely taken out of the house.

Even after children have been in a childcare program for a while, continue to mentally compare observations of practices with the licensing rules you read during the decision-making process. Do any practices or policies of the program not conform to the licensing rules? Discuss any repeated discrepancies with the director. If the response is not satisfactory or no change occurs, call the childcare licensing agency.

Be sensitive to any changes in children's behaviors. Overly passive or aggressive behavior; ripped, torn, or missing clothes; or bruises or other physical marks may be signs of neglect or abuse or just the result of a child's play. Ask the child and caregiver for an explanation. Do the answers match? Assure the child that he or she did nothing wrong—do not punish or blame him or her. Listen to what children say about their caregivers, as well as what they say about other children. When a child tells you he or she does not want to be with someone, there may be a good reason. If children report touching or being exposed to any other adult sexual behavior, believe them. Children rarely make up stories about sexual abuse. Preschool-aged children cannot make up stories when they have not had any first-hand experience with that activity. Take children seriously and call CPS if it seems that a child has been mistreated in any way. However, remember that child abuse in childcare is rare.

Most importantly, have a positive attitude about your choice. If you feel good about your childcare arrangement, usually your child will, too.

Choosing In-Home Childcare Providers

While many families choose out-of-home settings, other families may select full-time, in-home caregivers. For these families, keeping children in their own home is the ideal option. Parents may want to use in-home care if their child has special physical, mental, or emotional needs and requires a special form of care. In-home care may also be particularly suited for the family that can afford it and needs childcare at night or for long and/or irregular hours. The main difficulty of choosing in-home care is finding the best fit among caregiver, family, and costs.

Parents may choose a placement service to screen applicants and give them the names of individuals to interview. Placement agencies will be expected to do a background check before giving parents the names of potential caregivers. A background check, regardless of who does it, should include a CPS and law enforcement check for child maltreatment and any other felony conviction. Parents should be sure to call all references provided, asking specific questions relating to the individual's ability to care for children. Suggested reference questions are listed in **Table 8-6**. Notice that there are no right or wrong responses to these questions; they are merely used for gathering data with which to make a decision. Also, note that written, nonconfidential references are not appropriate because they are seldom objective. Parents should always require confidential written references. When requesting college transcripts, always require an official copy directly from the college or university. Parents of infants, toddlers, and

---

Table 8-6. Questions to Ask References

For Professional References
— When and where have you observed the candidate working with children?
— What skills does this candidate demonstrate in working with children?
— What is this person's philosophy of discipline? Please give examples of how he/she uses a variety of discipline techniques based on the child and the situation.
— Does this candidate demonstrate that he or she has realistic expectations for children's behavior? Please provide some examples.
— Does this candidate encourage independence and allow children to make choices for themselves (as opposed to directing their activities and controlling their play)?
— Does this individual ask for support from the supervisor or colleagues when needed?
— Does this candidate enjoy caring for children?
— How long did the candidate work with you? Why did he or she leave? Who was his/her immediate supervisor?
— How well does the candidate communicate ideas and opinions to others?
— How does the candidate handle frustration and criticism on the job?
— Does the candidate show interest in training or other means of improving his/her skills and knowledge?
— How does the candidate communicate with parents?
— Have there been any complaints regarding the candidate's care of children?
— Have you ever seen the candidate lose her or his temper? If so, describe the circumstance.
— To your knowledge, has the candidate had any criminal convictions? If so, what are they?
— Would you rehire this individual to work with children?

For Personal References
— How long have you known the candidate?
— In what capacity do you know the candidate?
— Where and when have you observed the candidate with children?
— What skills do you feel he or she demonstrates in working with children?
— How does the candidate respond in stressful situations?
— To your knowledge, has the candidate had any criminal convictions? If so, what are they?

Adapted from Koralek.[10]

---

preschool-aged children should consider whether the individual has the physical ability to get down on the child's level (down on the floor), lift the child, supervise the child visually, and hear the child. Remember that even though the screening process is time consuming, it is vital for exposing any misrepresentation or dangerous backgrounds.

Desirable traits for the in-home caregivers include knowledge of child growth and development as well as demonstrated nurturing skills. An important part of nurturing is unconditional acceptance of children and providing guidance for positive behaviors. With an understanding of normal growth and development, caregivers anticipate children's capabilities, fears, frustrations, and behaviors. This knowledge allows caregivers to plan and avoid situations that could cause problems.

As with any business transaction, parents and in-home childcare providers need a formal written agreement. Having a written job description and discussing a personnel policy in detail before employment begins will prevent later problems. These agreements should be specific about pay, hours of employment, vacation, emergency illnesses, sick leave, personal business days, meals, transportation, and any other special considerations, such as a smoking policy or the type of dress required. Making a list of specific "house rules" may prevent misunderstanding as the relationship develops. When the children become old enough to understand, include them when preparing the house rules to ensure that they know the mutually agreed-upon expectations. Written messages verifying verbal messages may facilitate communication as well.

CHOOSING PART-TIME CAREGIVERS

Choosing a part-time babysitter for the evening or day is also important. Some interview questions that will be helpful in the decision are listed in **Table 8-7**. Derry Koralek, in guidelines the National Center on Child Abuse and Neglect distributed for use by childcare providers, strongly recommends that the interview for all childcare workers, including those who are part-time, include an approximately 1-hour

---

Table 8-7. Suggested Interview Questions

— What activities would you expect a 6-year-old child (or the age of your child) to enjoy?
— What do you enjoy doing outdoors with children?
— What type of discipline did your parents use with you when you were young? How effective was it? What were you disciplined for?
— How do you think children learn? Give an example of how you would set up a learning experience for a child.
— How would you settle a dispute between two 2 year olds who want the same toy at the same time? Two 5 year olds?
— What would you plan to feed a 6-year-old child (or the age of your child) over the course of a day?
— If you are a parent, what type of discipline do you use with your children? When do you remember using discipline, and in what situations?
— Which of your personality traits do you consider assets to caregiving?
— How would you describe your own childhood?
— What are your interests or hobbies?

Adapted from Koralek.[10]

observation of the candidate with the child or children.[10] Ideally, the candidates should be asked to arrive prepared to conduct an activity with the child or children and told that they will be asked to interact with children during a free play period. **Table 8-8** offers an observation guide for parents to use during this interaction. If they do not know the individual personally, requesting references and a background check is appropriate.

Table 8-8. Positive Observations When Candidates Are Working With Children
The candidate for your childcare provider should. . . — Observe the children and ask questions or interact with them in ways that promote thinking. — Have realistic expectations for the children's stages of development. — Demonstrate a sense of humor. — Show interest, enthusiasm, warmth, and patience in working with the children. — Use positive techniques to guide children's behavior. — Show a willingness to participate in all kinds of activities and routines. — Play with the children. — Comfort children who are distressed. — Appear comfortable caring for young children and seem to be enjoying him- or herself. *Adapted from Koralek.*[10]

An issue that sometimes arises when parents are considering short episodes of baby-sitting is how old the babysitter should be. When making this decision, parents should consider the age of their own child, the amount of care he or she will need, the maturity of the babysitter, and the amount of time the babysitter will be supervising the child. Several organizations provide babysitting courses and certifications for adolescents who want to provide short-term care for children. These are strongly encouraged by child health professionals and include programs from the American Red Cross and the Boys & Girls Club of America. No concrete rules exist for determining the exact age at which a child can safely supervise another child, but below are 2 local governmental guidelines as examples:

— Dakota County, Minnesota[11]

 — "It is acceptable for children ages 11 to 14 to babysit, with the expectation that the parent, guardian, or caretaker will be returning to supervise the children later that same day."

 — "It is acceptable for ages 15 and older to babysit younger children for more than 24 hours."

— Prince William County, Virginia[12]

 — "Ages 12 to 13 may babysit children up to 4 hours."

 — "Ages 14 to 15 may babysit children over 4 hours—not overnight or weekends."

 — "Ages 16 to 17 may babysit children overnight or over the weekends."

CONCLUSION

Many children spend several hours in childcare each day for several years. The quality of that care is important to their emotional, social, and cognitive development. Quality care is not merely luck; research shows that certain provider characteristics predict positive outcomes for children. Childcare centers and childcare homes that are both licensed and accredited have more of the characteristics that predict positive outcomes. Parents should ask many questions about the caregiver, the facility, and the activities before choosing a childcare provider—their children are depending upon them to collect good information, compare various options, make a good decision, and stay involved so that they receive safe, developmentally appropriate care.

REFERENCES

1. Shope TR, Aronson S. Improving the health and safety of children in nonparental early education and child care. *Pediatr Rev*. 2005;26:86-95.

2. What kinds of care are available? Child Care Aware Web site. Available at: http://www.childcareaware.org/en/care. Accessed March 15, 2006.

3. Fiene R. *13 Indicators of Quality Child Care: Research Update*. Washington, DC: US Dept of Health & Human Services; 2002.

4. Hyman IA. *The Case Against Spanking: How to Discipline Your Child Without Hitting*. San Francisco, Calif: Jossey-Bass Publishers; 1997.

5. Early years are learning years helping young children start school. The National Association for the Education of Young Children Web site. Available at: www.naeyc.org/ece/2005/06.asp. Accessed June 21, 2006.

6. National Child Care Information Center. Choosing a child care center or family child care provider. Vienna, Va: National Child Care Information Center; 2005. Available at: http://www.nccic.org/poptopics/choosecare.html. Accessed March 15, 2006.

7. State profiles. National Child Care Information Center Web site. Available at: http://nccic.org/statedata/statepro/index.html. Accessed March 15, 2006.

8. Individual states' child care licensure regulations. National Resource Center for Health and Safety in Child Care Web site. Available at: http://nrc.uchsc.edu/STATES/states.htm. Accessed March 15, 2006.

9. National Association for the Education of Young Children Web site. Available at: http://www.naeyc.org/accreditation/default.asp. Accessed June 29, 2006.

10. Koralek D. Caregivers of young children: preventing and responding to child maltreatment. Washington, DC: US Dept of Health & Human Services; 1992. Available at: http://www.child-welfare.gov/pubs/usermanuals/caregive/caregive.pdf. Accessed June 29, 2006.

11. At what age may a child be left home alone and for how long? Dakota County Attorney's Office Web site. Available at: http://www.co.dakota.mn.us/attorney/FAQ/Faq19.htm. Accessed March 15, 2006.

12. Child protective services investigations and family assessments. Prince William County, Virginia Web site. Available at: http://www.co.prince-william.va.us/default.aspx?topic=040041000120000757. Accessed March 15, 2006.

Chapter 9

SAFETY FOR CHILDREN ON THE INTERNET

Maria D. McColgan, MD
Angelo P. Giardino, MD, PhD, MPH, FAAP

As the use of computers and the Internet increases, their potential risks to children are becoming clearer. The same technology that offers great opportunities to access vast amounts of valuable information and enhance our children's education and creative exploration also creates the potential for people to harm our children. Thus, parents and caregivers need to understand the potential benefits and risks of children using computers and the Internet.

Computer and Internet use have become so ingrained in our daily routines that even young children rely on them. Connections to computers and the Internet are now pervasive enough to be available in private homes, public and private schools, and free libraries. Most children aged 8 through 18 years have used a computer, and 96% of them have gone online, where they spend an average of 48 minutes per day.[1] Because of this pervasiveness, the risks of the Internet are much greater for children than most parents are aware.

Simply forbidding or even restricting a child's Internet access is unrealistic: Many schools require Internet use, and it can be a valuable research tool. A better idea is for parents and caregivers to teach children to use the Internet wisely and safely, just as they teach them to drive carefully.

KNOWING THE INTERNET

Parents must be familiar with computers and the Internet so they can monitor and understand their child's computer and Internet use. More than three quarters of parents agree that being a "watchdog," or a "guide to good content," is the most important role for parents to play in terms of supervising their children's Internet use.[2] However, a challenge is that parents are not always as computer savvy as are their children—something most parents will freely admit to. Only 31% of parents believe themselves to be advanced users or experts, while 44% fall at an intermediate level and 25% at beginner.[3]

The Internet is a worldwide interconnection of computers via phone and cable lines. It has grown into a global communication tool for academic, commercial, and other applications, connecting over 100 countries and millions of computers. Among the services supported by this network are e-mail and the World Wide Web (WWW). Nicknames for the Internet include "the net," "the information superhighway," and "cyberspace."

All it takes to connect to the Internet are a computer, modem, and phone or cable line. An Internet user can choose whatever Internet Service Provider (ISP) they wish.

Examples of popular ISPs are America Online (AOL), Microsoft Network (MSN), and Verizon. ISPs charge users a monthly fee in return for access to the Internet, a software package, a username, a password, and an access phone number. Typical software packages include a browser, such as Microsoft Internet Explorer or Netscape Navigator, which is used to locate and display Web pages. *Web pages* are individual documents made up of text, pictures, music, and more that can be accessed via the Internet. A *Web site* is a group of multiple Web pages that are organized together. Once a user has opened a browser, he or she can use a search engine, such as Google or Yahoo!, to find information. A *search engine* is a program that searches the Internet for and then provides a list of Web pages that involve words specified by the user. For example, a user who types "movie showtimes" into a search engine will be given a list of Web pages that contain movie showtimes.

Americans are deeply worried about criminal activity on the Internet. Ninety-two percent of Americans say they are concerned about child pornography on the Internet, which 50% consider the Internet's most heinous crime.[4] Additionally, in the survey *A Nation Online*, 68% of respondents said they were more concerned about their children's exposure to material on the Internet than to material on television, while 26% were equally concerned with the two.[5] In the National School Boards Foundation's (NSBF) *Safe and Smart* report, parents' 3 top concerns regarding what their children might encounter on the Internet were pornography, undesirable adult contacts, and violent or hateful content.[2]

Parents do have ways of monitoring their children's Internet use. A study revealed that 63% of the polled parents checked their computer's history function to see what sites their children had visited, 48% checked files and diskettes, 44% made their children ask for permission to go on the Internet, and 39% had instituted family rules about the number of hours their children could spend on the Internet.[5]

Although some parents are discouraged by not knowing as much about computers as their children do, that gap can be used to the parents' advantage. Parents should let their children teach them about the Internet, showing them the sites they visit and enjoy. Children can be a valuable source of information and will often relish the opportunity to be their parents' teacher.

RISKS ASSOCIATED WITH INTERNET USE

Since the scope of available information and services on the Internet is constantly changing, it is impossible to describe every possible risk. Instead, this chapter will address some of the more predominant risks, along with various ways for parents to protect their children from them. Ultimately, monitoring a child's computer and Internet use in various ways will minimize the risk posed to them, whether from inappropriate or dangerous material or from a stranger the child "met" on the Internet.

CHAT ROOMS, E-MAIL, AND INSTANT MESSAGING

Allowing children to use chat rooms, e-mail, and instant messaging unsupervised creates the potential for them to be unknowingly solicited by child predators while in the "safety" of their own home. A *chat room* is a site on the WWW where any computer users can type messages to each other in real time, creating an online conversation, or *chat*.

Chat rooms are one of the most popular areas on the Internet. Each chat room is designed for the discussion of a single, specific topic, and the rooms are listed by name to signal what that topic is. In 2001, 55% of children aged 12 through 17 years who went online visited chat rooms.[6] To participate in a chat, an Internet user selects a screen name, or **handle**, by which he or she will be known. Since acquiring a screen name does not require any verification of identity, a chat room visitor can easily assume a disguise. For example, an adult man can use his screen name to pretend to be a teen-aged girl, and none of the other members in the chat room would be able to tell.

After selecting a room, the screen name appears in the room, often with a profile the user created. The profile displays basic information about the user, which can be read by every other person in the chat room. Anyone can have access to the information in another user's profile, which may include as little as the child's age and sex or as much as the child's address and school.

In addition to group chats, the Internet also allows users to run one-on-one chats, which are visible only to those conversing. These chats allow a child sexual predator easy and private access to the intended victim. The predator can assess the safety of the situation by asking questions such as where the child is using the computer—the bedroom or a common area of the house—or whether the child is home alone. The predator can talk with the child at great length with little risk of being discovered, beginning with innocent topics and moving gradually to inappropriate material. The predator may send pornography over the Internet to feel out and break down the intended victim's inhibitions. Child sexual offenders, according to most law enforce-ment agencies, are experts at "grooming" children—befriending them, talking to them, discovering their interests and weaknesses, and then exploiting them. Additionally, the Internet aids the grooming process by allowing the child sexual offender to obtain information from a child anonymously. If rebuffed by the child, the child sexual offender can move on by ending the conversation, with little fear of being traced and apprehended. If the child expresses interest, the child sexual offender can then use the Internet to lure the child to a meeting place. Sexual assaults, which occur after grooming, are the end result of a process of seduction in which the child sexual offender uses the victim's vulnerability, naiveté, and interest in exploration against them.

As of 2000, 60% of teenagers received e-mail or **instant messages** (a form of accelerated e-mail that allows for rapid exchanges in a back-and-forth fashion) from a stranger, and, surprisingly, 63% responded to the message.[7] Nearly 20% had been the targets of unwanted solicitation during a 1-year period. The highest risk was for girls, older teen-agers, troubled youths, those who used the Internet frequently, those who participated in chat room discussions, and those who communicated with strangers online.

As the perpetrator establishes trust with a child, the requests become more aggressive. Types of solicitations might include the following:

— Requests for personal information, such as name, age, grade in school, or likes and dislikes

— Propositions for **cybersex**, a form of fantasy sex via an interactive chat-room session in which participants describe sexual activity and sometimes disrobe and masturbate

— Requests to meet in person or make other contact offline

Here are real-life examples of aggressive solicitations[7]:

— A 14-year-old girl reported that men claiming to be 18 to 20 years old sent her instant messages asking her measurements and other questions about her appearance when they were aware of her age.

— A 12-year-old girl said that people told her sexual things that they were doing to each other and asked her to "play with herself."

— A 15-year-old girl said that an older man kept "bothering" her and asked if she was a virgin and if he could meet her.

— A 13-year-old boy said that a girl asked him how big his "privates" were and wanted him to "jack off."

— A 13-year-old boy said that a man sent him a drawing of the man having sex with a dog.

Although many of the children report these solicitations as stressful or embarrassing, only 10% of the solicitations were reported to the police, ISP, or other official. Also, more than two thirds of the parents and over three quarters of the children and teenagers did not know where they could report the incidents.[7]

Web Sites
A Web site can be found on virtually any topic that one may imagine; therefore, another major risk of the Internet is related to accessing dangerous or erroneous content on particular Web sites.

Exposure to Sexual Content
One study[7] showed that among 1501 children and teenagers between the ages of 10 and 17 years who used the Internet regularly, 25% reported at least one unwanted exposure to sexual material in the previous year. Ninety-four percent of the exposures were to images of unclothed people, 38% of images showed people having sex, and 8% involved violence in addition to the sexual content. Access to the unwanted material came as a result of searches in 47% of instances, misspelled addresses in 17%, and links within a Web site in another 17%. Thirty-nine percent of the children and teenagers told their parents of the incidents, and 44% told no one. Twenty-three percent of the children and teenagers reported that the exposure was very or extremely upsetting, and 20% were very or extremely embarrassed.

General Health Information
Millions of Web sites disseminate health information, and over 93 million people turn to the Internet for this information.[8] Approximately 50% to 75% of online youth use the Internet for health-related information.[6,9,10] In one study, 49% of 10th graders had used the Internet to access health-related information.[10] The Pew Foundation found that youths aged 15 to 17 years are significantly more likely to have looked up health information (32%) than youths aged 12 to 14 years (18%).[6] The 2001 Kaiser survey of people aged 15 through 24 years found that 75% had used the Internet at least once to research health-related topics and 39% had changed their personal behavior because of health information they found online.[11] Adolescents most frequently explored information on specific diseases, including cancer and diabetes; sexually transmitted diseases; diet, fitness, and exercise; and sexual behaviors.[6,9,10] Adolescent girls were also interested in birth control, physical and sexual abuse, and violence.[10] The Internet provides ease and anonymity, which is appealing when seeking advice on sensitive topics.

Access to appropriate and correct health-related information on the Internet is an area of concern shared by many health experts. In a study observing 68 adolescent health-related searches, only 69% of the searches successfully located correct and useful answers to the health-related question.[12] Furthermore, the adolescents paid little or no attention to the source of the answer. In the vast majority of cases, once an answer was located, it was simply assumed to be correct. Parents and caregivers may want to take the opportunity to encourage children and adolescents to be critical of the sites they visit. Parents may want to recommend health care Web sites of well-respected national organizations, such as the American Academy of Pediatrics (http://www.aap.org) and the American Academy of Child and Adolescent Psychiatry (http://www.aacap.org).

Eating Disorders

Sixty-three percent of adolescents search the Internet for information on body image and nutrition.[9] As with any other health-related topic, a search for "anorexia" or "bulimia" will yield thousands of sites that offer information and resources for getting help. However, the Internet can also provide information that is harmful. Change the search topic to "pro-ana" (pro-anorexia) or "pro-mia" (pro-bulimia) and the search will reveal an underground network of anorexics and bulimics who share information on how to be a "better" anorexic or bulimic.[9] In other words, these Web sites encourage and assist those who are already drastically underweight to lose even more weight. Although disclaimers on the sites clearly state that they are not intended for those who are not already anorexic, such claims only add allure and mystery to visitors. The authors of the sites often view themselves as an elite group who demonstrate power by exerting self-control over their bodies. However, their messages are very damaging to those who listen, particularly to teenagers: 86% of persons with eating disorders report the onset of illness before 20 years of age.[13] In July 2001, the National Association of Anorexia Nervosa and Related Eating Disorders became aware of these sites and has actively campaigned for their removal. Many servers, such as Yahoo!, have agreed to remove these sites, but some still remain active.[13]

Sexuality, Puberty, and Sexually Transmitted Diseases

In 2001, a Pew Foundation report found that 18% of online youths said they have looked online for sensitive sexual information and 26% of all teenagers online think the Internet is helpful in this regard.[6] As many as 84% of adolescents reported that they most frequently use the Internet for sexual information, including that on sexual activities, birth control, pregnancy, and sexually transmitted diseases.[6,9,10] Even with parental controls, children can access various Web sites with inappropriate sexual content. Teenagers can also share information in chat rooms, which can potentially lead to widespread sharing of erroneous information and myths. One study found that young adults who meet sexual partners online may be at greater risk for sexually transmitted diseases than those who do not.[14]

Suicide

A child with suicidal thoughts who uses the Internet to search for support groups or places to get help may end up visiting one of many Web sites that actually condones suicide and describes ways to commit suicide.[15] These sites may discourage the child from seeking professional help. Children may also visit these Web sites if they want to find the "best" way to commit suicide. One 14-year-old boy researched various methods of suicide and types of poisonous plants online. He died after intentionally ingesting poisonous plants he found in his parents' garden.[16] In another incident, a 20-year-old man reported learning his methods of attempted suicide via the Internet.[17]

Chat rooms and other means of anonymously meeting strangers have reportedly been linked to suicides. A 25-year-old woman, after recovering from an attempted suicide, reported Internet contact with a person who encouraged her to commit suicide. This person turned out to be a 33-year-old woman fascinated with psychology and parapsychology.[18] Reports of suicide pacts via the Internet have also been reported.[19]

Illegal Drugs and Raves

In a study of young adult users of ecstasy (a common name for 3,4-methylenedioxy-methamphetamine, or MDMA), about half used the Internet to find information about the drug, with younger users more likely to do so.[20] Information on recreational drug use is widely available via the Internet, which facilitates the free and easy exchange of ideas, opinions, and unedited and unreferenced information of all kinds.[21] Common search engines can easily find many Web sites that offer information on particular drugs' effects, drug dosing, addiction, mixing drugs, and detection times for drug tests. Other sites provide tips such as "recipes" for illegal drugs like methamphetamines and ecstasy or how to "avoid a bad trip." Children can also arrange to purchase drugs illegally via the Internet.

Many illegal drugs are considered "club drugs" and are widely used at teenage dance parties called "raves." An online rave community, which is well aware of the use of drugs at raves, provides information regarding raves, including online discussions and party reviews.[22] Harm-reduction Web sites, such as DanceSafe (http://www.dancesafe.org), try to make attending raves as safe as possible. These sites provide information on specific drugs, their ingredients, their effects, and potential dangers.[22] These sites were visited 4 times more frequently than government-sponsored Web sites.[20]

Dangerous or Illegal Activity

Incredibly, there are Web sites with instructions on how to commit almost any illegal activity. A search of the phrase "how to make a gun" provides sites on how to make a tattoo gun, a stun gun, gun powder, fireworks and other explosives, and even how to make any gun silent. A child can arrange to purchase weapons illegally via the Internet. A child can also learn to be a computer hacker or to send computer viruses, simply by searching for "how-to" sites with instructions. A search for "how to kill someone" provides numerous sites with detailed information on whom to kill, the weaknesses of the human body, and how to carry out the act.

Hate Crimes

The Federal government defines a *hate crime* as "a crime in which the defendant selects a victim, or in the case of a property crime, the property that is the object of the crime, because of the actual or perceived race, color, religion, national origin, ethnicity, gender, disability, or sexual orientation of any person."[23] According to Partners Against Hate, 33% of all known hate crime offenders are younger than 18 years, and 29% of all hate crime offenders are aged 18 through 24 years.[24] Thirty-one percent of all violent crime offenders and 46% of the property offenders are younger than 18 years, while 30% of all victims of bias-motivated aggravated assaults and 34% of the victims of simple assault are younger than 18 years.[24]

The Internet allows individuals to openly or anonymously perpetuate hate via Web sites or mass e-mailings. For example, in September 1996, an expelled 21-year-old college student sent a threatening e-mail to 60 Asian students at the University of California, Irvine. In the e-mail, the student expressed hatred for Asians, threatening to hunt down and kill all Asians on campus if they did not leave the university, and the student signed the message "Asian Hater."[23] Eventually, the student admitted that he sent the threatening message, and he was charged with and convicted of violating federal civil rights laws.

Unfortunately, many Web sites with similar racial divides and messages of hate exist today and are protected under the First Amendment right of free speech. These are numerous sites touting white power, Nazism, black power, and others.

WHAT PARENTS CAN DO TO REDUCE THE RISKS OF THE INTERNET

There are many strategies a parent can use to help protect their children while on the Internet, ranging from simple conversations between parent and child to sophisticated filtering software.

DIRECT PARENTAL SUPERVISION

Of all of the available mechanisms for protecting children on the Internet, none are as powerful as communication and direct parental supervision. Parents and children do not often talk about privacy on the Web and when divulging information is and is not appropriate. Children and their parents do not necessarily hold the same attitudes or even recall the same discussions about the topic within the family. A study by Turow and Nir showed that parent-child conversations about Web privacy issues were limited to "don't give out your name" or "don't talk to strangers," leaving children unprepared to deal with issues such as bartering information for free gifts or extending trust to a person without any factual data as to who that person really is.[3]

Table 9-1 lists tips for parents supervising their children on the Internet. One is to have and enforce rules about Internet usage. A list of rules might include the following:

— Never reveal your password to anyone online, not even to online service staff members.

— Never reveal identifying information—real name (first or last), family member names, home address, details of a parent's work, school or team names, telephone number, social security number, or credit card number—in a chat room, a bulletin board message, or an e-mail to someone you do not know.

— Never accept offers of merchandise or information or give out your street address, even if for deliveries, without getting your parents' permission.

— Never send a photograph of yourself or offer a physical description of yourself or family members over the Internet.

— Never continue a conversation that makes you feel uncomfortable or becomes personal. Just "hang up" on the conversation by going to another area of the Internet. Tell your parents what happened.

— Never answer an e-mail that is suggestive, obscene, rude, or makes you feel uncomfortable in any way. Tell your parents if you come across such messages and forward the messages to the service provider. It is not your fault if you get such a message.

— Never arrange to meet someone in person whom you have met online. If your parents do agree to a meeting, make sure you arrange it for a public spot and take a parent along.

— Be careful when responding to e-mail. Return addresses can be falsified to make a message look innocent. If you cannot verify the sender, do not answer it.

— Remember: No matter how friendly someone seems on the Internet, that person is still a stranger. The person may be an adult pretending to be a child.

REPORTING ONLINE ENCOUNTERS

Parents must be able to recognize dangers and know what to do when they are encountered. Almost 70% of parents do not know where to report troublesome Internet

---

Table 9-1. Tips for Parents Supervising Children on the Internet

— Explain to your children why you are interested in their online activities.
  — Explain that there are risks involved in using the Internet and describe some of the more common ones. For example, explain that a person they chat with online is still a stranger, and someone they think is a child might actually be an adult with a history of criminal activity.
  — Do not let their desire for privacy overtake their need for parental supervision.
  — Ask your children to show you where they go online, and stay in touch during their online sessions.
— Become familiar with computers and the Internet.
  — Use the Internet and become familiar with the online services your children access.
  — Read literature about the Internet and its potential dangers for children.
  — Talk about your concerns with other parents.
— Have and enforce rules about Internet use.
  — Post the rules near the computer.
  — Specify the type of sites children can visit.
  — Specify the amount of time allowed online per day for fun activities.
  — Specify the time of day children are allowed online. For example, curb late-night usage in teenagers, especially usage of online chat rooms.
  — Set and enforce consequences for when the rules are broken.
— Keep the computer in a public place in the house. Allowing children to keep a computer with Internet access in their bedroom is particularly dangerous because it allows them ample opportunity for secrecy.
— Tell your children that they must not give out personal information such as their name, address, e-mail, phone, age, grade in school, or likes and dislikes.
  — In a study by the British NOP Research Group of 4 million children aged 7 through 17 years who surf the net, 29% would freely give out their home address and 14% would freely give out their e-mail address when asked.[25]
  — Explain to children some of the illegal or dangerous ways a stranger could use the personal information.
— Tell your children that they cannot send pictures of themselves to a stranger online.
  — Explain that they never know what a person will do with the picture.
  — Because the image would be digital, a person could share it with others or even modify the image to make it sexually explicit.
— Go with your child if he or she wants to arrange to meet someone they met online.
  — Explain to your child that if an online friend truly wants to be a friend, then there is no need for secrecy.
  — If you and your child decide to meet face to face with someone he or she met online, be sure to meet in a public place.

episodes; an additional 20% have heard of a place to report but are not able to remember the name.[3] Only 10% can name a specific name or authority.[7]

The National Center for Missing & Exploited Children wants to be alerted to the presence of any illegal material online, such as child pornography, threatening messages, or evidence of criminal action. Depending on the severity, illegal material and inappropriate solicitations can also be reported to the ISP or the police.

ONLINE RESOURCES FOR PARENTS

There are many Web sites available to help parents and children with online safety. For example, Netsmartz is an interactive educational tool for parents and children with valuable information about Internet use, resources, and links to other sites. Netsmartz also provides real-life stories of online encounters that led to dangerous situations. Examples include a 15-year-old girl who took a 36-hour bus ride to meet with a stranger she met online and another teenager who left home to meet with a stranger she met online, who then turned out to be a convicted murderer.

BLOCKING SOFTWARE

Most ISPs and software manufacturers provide **blocking software** to keep children from accessing certain sites and/or to document what sites a computer's user has visited on the Internet.[26] However, no matter how much help blocking software may be to parents trying to monitor their children's online activity, it does not replace other forms of parental supervision.

Three types of blocking can be used to filter out sites inappropriate for children.[27] **Human analysis** creates a customized list of sites that are permitted and prohibited. However, this method is generally impractical; the number of Web sites published each day can far exceed the ability of software companies to review and categorize them.[28] **Software analysis** screens a site's content and filters out those with objectionable phrases or images. However, this method is problematic, too, since the filtering may block out many legitimate sites. The third form, **site labeling**, relies on the voluntary labeling of Web sites by their owners. The labeling system is based on the Internet Content Rating Association's (ICRA) system. The major drawback with site labeling is that not all sites have labeled their content and as a result will not be blocked, even if their content is objectionable. Users can set their filter to block all unlabeled sites, but a large number of legitimate sites will also be blocked. Consider consulting computer magazines to find the software that is right for you and your family.

CONCLUSION

As with the many other dangers our children face as they are growing, the Internet demands precautionary measures. Adults must teach children to navigate the Internet safely. By understanding the dangers facing them, children can be prepared to deal with solicitation, exposure to unwanted material, and other concerns. By fostering open communication about the Internet, children will feel comfortable coming to parents to discuss any hazards they encounter.

REFERENCES

1. Robert DF, Foehr UG, Rideout V. *Generation M: Media in the Lives of 8-18 Year-old–Report*. Kaiser Family Foundation. March 2005. Available at: http://www.kff.org/entmedia/upload/Generation-M-Media-in-the-Lives-of-8-18-Year-oldsReport.pdf. Accessed March 20, 2006.

2. National School Boards Foundation. Research and guidelines for children's use of the Internet. *Safe Smart*. 1999. Available at: http://www.nsbf.org/safe-smart/full-report.htm. Accessed March 20, 2006.

3. Turow J, Nir L. *The Internet and the Family 2000: The View From Parents, the View From Kids*. Philadelphia: The Annenberg Public Policy Center of the University of Pennsylvania; 2000.

4. Fox S, Lewis O. *Fear of Online Crime: Americans Support FBI Interception of*

Criminal Suspects' Email and New Laws to Protect Online Privacy. Washington, DC: Pew Internet & American Life Project; 2001. Available at: http://www.pewinternet. org/pdfs/PIP_Fear_of_crime.pdf. Accessed March 20, 2006.

5. US Department of Commerce. *A Nation Online: How Americans Are Expanding Their Use of the Internet.* Washington, DC: Economic and Statistics Administration, National Telecommunications and Information Administration; 2002:1-95.

6. Lenhart A, Rainie L, Lewis O. *Teenage Life Online: The Rise of the Instant-Message Generation and the Internet's Impact on Friendships and Family Relationships*. Washington, DC: Pew Internet & American Life; 2001. Available at: http://www. pewinternet.org/pdfs/PIP_Teens_Report.pdf. Accessed March 20, 2006.

7. Finkelhor D, Mitchell KJ, Wolak J. *Online Victimization: A Report on the Nation's Youth*. Alexandria, Va: National Center for Missing & Exploited Children, American Bar Association on Children and the Law; March 2001.

8. Fox S, Fallows D. *Internet Health Resources: Health Searches and Email Have Become Commonplace, but There is Room for Improvement in Searches and Overall Internet Access*. Washington, DC: Pew Internet & American Life Project; 2003. Available at: http://www.pewinternet.org/PPF/r/95/report_display.asp. Accessed March 8, 2006.

9. Skinner H, Biscope S, Poland B, Goldberg E. How adolescents use technology for health information: implications for health professionals from focus group studies. *J Med Internet Res*. 2003;5:e32.

10. Borzekowski DL, Rickert VI. Adolescent cybersurfing for health information: a new resource that crosses barriers. *Arch Pediatr Adolesc Med*. 2001;155:813-817.

11. Rideout VJ. *Generation RX.com: How Young People Use the Internet for Health Information*. Menlo Park, Calif: Henry J Kaiser Family Foundation; 2001. Available at: http://www.kff.org/entmedia/upload/Toplines.pdf. Accessed January 9, 2006.

12. Hansen D, Derry HA, Resnick PJ, Richardson CR. Adolescents searching for health information on the Internet: an observational study. *J Med Internet Res*. 2003;5:e25.

13. Eating disorder info & resources. National Association of Anorexia Nervosa and Associated Disorders Web site. Available at: http://www.anad.org/site/anadweb/ content.php?type=1&id=6982. Accessed July 10, 2006.

14. McFarlane M, Bull SS, Rietmeijer CA. Young adults on the Internet: risk behaviors for sexually transmitted diseases and HIV. *J Adolesc Health*. 2002;31:11-16.

15. Dobson R. Internet sites may encourage suicide. Editorial. *BMJ*. 1999;319:337.

16. Wehner F, Gawatz O. Suicidal yew poisoning—from Caesar to today—or suicide instructions on the Internet. *Arch Kriminol*. 2003;211:19-26.

17. Prior TI. Suicide methods from the Internet. *Am J Psychiatry*. 2004;161:1500-1501.

18. Chodorowski Z, Sein Anand J. Internet as a means of persuading a patient to commit a suicide. *Przegl Lek*. 2002;59:375-376.

19. Rajagopal S. Suicide pacts and the Internet. *BMJ*. 2004;329:1298-1299.

20. Falck RS, Carlson, RG, Wang J, Siegal HA. Sources of information about MDMA (3,4-methylenedioxymethamphetamine): perceived accuracy, importance and implications for prevention among young adult users. *Drug Alcohol Depend*. 2004;74:45-54.

21. Wax PM. Just a click away: recreational drug Web sites on the Internet. *Pediatrics*. 2002;109:e96.

22. Sullivan G. Raving on the internet. *CMAJ*. 2000:162:1864.

23. Kaplan JE, Moss MP; Lieberman ML, ed. *Investigating Hate Crimes on the Internet*. Washington, DC: Partners Against Hate; September 2003. Available at: http://www.partnersagainsthate.org/publications/investigating_hc.pdf. Accessed July 10, 2006.

24. Home page. Partners Against Hate Web site. Available at: http://www.partnersagainsthate.org. Accessed July 10, 2006.

25. Child Internet safety: tips for parents. State of Virginia Attorney General's Office Web site. Available at: http://www.oag.state.va.us/KEY_ISSUES/PREDATORS/Internet_Tips_for_Parents.html. Accessed August 2, 2006.

26. Gallow D. Filtering tools, education, and the parent: ingredients for surfing safely on the information super-highway. *APSAC Advisor*. 1998;11:23-25.

27. Digital chaperones for kids: which Internet filters protect the best? Which get in the way? *Consumer Rep*. March 2001:20-23.

28. Internet safety: what you always wanted to know about filtering software but were afraid to ask. Family Guide Book Web site. Available at: http://www.familyguidebook.com/filtering.html. Accessed March 20, 2006.

Chapter 10

CHILD PROTECTIVE SERVICES, MENTAL HEALTH ISSUES, AND THE MULTIDISCIPLINARY TEAM APPROACH

Angelo P. Giardino, MD, PhD, MPH, FAAP

As described in previous chapters, reports of suspected child maltreatment are typically made to the county or state child protective services (CPS) agency. In some cases and according to some state laws, referral to the police is also required. Following a report, CPS agencies have a fairly standard way of gathering the information needed to investigate the case. They also have a systematic way of determining risk to a child's safety and the family's ability to meet the child's needs. This determination may lead to mental health services being provided to the child and family. This multistep process involving multiple disciplines best serves the children and families affected by child maltreatment.

REPORTS OF ABUSE

Children and families who become involved with CPS investigations commonly also require referral to mental health services. If the investigation determines that the report is *substantiated*, meaning that abuse or neglect actually has occurred, mental health services are essential because being victimized by a caregiver often causes significant psychological injury. In fact, the child and family may even be in need of mental health services if the report is unsubstantiated, because the suspicion and investigations themselves can be psychologically jarring. Children do vary in their emotional responses to abuse and neglect, and one factor that influences the response is the way in which nonabusive adults help them after the abuse and neglect come to light. These adults include nonabusive family members, family friends and supporters, teachers, coaches, ministers, and even laypersons that they come in contact with.

Each year, CPS agencies receive approximately 3.5 million reports of suspected child abuse and neglect.[1] These reports are processed, duplicate reports and already-known cases of abuse and neglect are weeded out, and the rest are investigated. In recent years, between 900 000 and 1 million cases have been substantiated annually.[1] When a case is considered unsubstantiated, it means the investigation did not produce enough information to confidently say abuse or neglect occurred. Some of the unsubstantiated cases are truly not cases of abuse and neglect, and some are cases in which maltreatment occurred but simply could not be proved. Thus, it is ideal to offer mental health services to families regardless of whether the case was officially substantiated. It is beneficial for children who may be in difficult circumstances to develop a helping relationship with a mental health professional. These professionals can help explore children's emotional health and wellness and maintain contact with them as events unfold after a report is made.

CASE EXAMPLE

Susan, a dedicated mother, was choking back tears and barely able to speak as she called the sexual abuse clinic. The operator could tell there was a crisis just by the tone of Susan's voice, even before she related what had happened.

It was 8:00 PM the prior evening when Susan had answered her doorbell. The woman at the front door introduced herself as a Department of Children and Family Services hotline investigator; she had received a report of sexual abuse perpetrated against Susan's 7-year-old son and was there to investigate. This news took Susan completely by surprise. She was unaware of her son ever having been abused and, in fact, had not even considered it a possibility. She felt as if she were dreaming, that something so awful could not really be happening.

As they continued talking, Susan slowly realized that this was no dream: There truly had been a report of abuse against her son. The investigator related that her son, Ray, had told his teacher about the abuse, who in turn contacted the proper authorities. The story disclosed was that the husband of Ray's babysitter had fondled Ray several times. This eventually evolved into the babysitter's husband trying to persuade Ray to masturbate him and perform oral sex on him. The next day, after a coincidental classroom discussion on "good touch, bad touch," Ray disclosed the incidents to his teacher. As a mandated reporter, the teacher appropriately followed her school protocol and reported the disclosure to the hotline. The hotline then sent an investigator to Susan's house, but, unfortunately, the school had been unable to contact Susan and her husband before the investigator arrived.

Once interviewed, it was evident to the investigator and Ray's parents that inappropriate sexual contact had occurred. Susan was devastated; she blamed herself for not realizing her son had been victimized. Distraught, Susan called the sexual abuse clinic, also known as the special assessment and management (SAM) clinic, with her crisis-generated questions and received some helpful answers:

— *Why didn't Ray tell me what was happening at the babysitter's home?* He is a child who developmentally is not mature enough to fully understand the situation and is acting as such rather than as a knowledgeable, empowered adult.

— *Does this mean I am a bad mother?* No, child abuse is a form of victimization that takes advantage of vulnerability. The person who is to blame is the perpetrator, not the people who are victimized by this harmful criminal activity.

— *What can I do in the future to encourage Ray to talk to me about problems?* Create an emotionally safe environment in which it is understood that discussions of difficult issues will be met with support.

— *How can I create such an environment?* By responding in a way that illustrates that his safety is a priority, that the lines of communication are open, and that his developmental needs are going to be met.

THE TEAM APPROACH TO CHILD MALTREATMENT CASES

The value of teamwork among various professionals who deal with child abuse and neglect has been recognized and advocated since as early as the 1970s. Such an approach benefits professionals by affording them with opportunities for:

— Improved information sharing.

— Shared decision making.

— Shared planning.

— Collaborative education.

— Mutual support.

When responding to child maltreatment cases, teams seek to be as coordinated and efficient as possible. If successful, their efforts will ideally produce the following desirable outcomes:

— Reduction in the number of interviews to which a child is subjected

— Minimization of the number of people involved in cases

— Enhanced evidence quality, both for criminal prosecution and civil litigation

— Provision of information essential to CPS and other family service organizations

— Decreased likelihood of conflicts among the various agencies involved

Because of how helpful teams can be in the investigative process, in the 1990s the Pew Health Professions Commission called for a reorganization of clinical training, centering on the necessity and long-term benefits of teams.[2]

One noteworthy, specific type of team is the ***multidisciplinary team*** (MDT). This formation is distinguished from ordinary teams in that its members come from a variety of professional backgrounds and disciplines. Also, these teams address child abuse and neglect not only on the level of specific cases, but also on the greater, broader community level. MDTs are often established and staffed at teaching hospitals in academic health sciences centers. Additionally, a number of MDTs have emerged within community settings staffed by social services agency staff and primary care practitioners. The benefits of an effective MDT include[3]:

— Reduced "system-inflicted" trauma to children and families during the investigation

— Increased agency performance, including enhanced accuracy of investigations and more appropriate interventions

— Efficient use of limited community resources

— Development of collaborative skills, making professionals more capable

— Recognition of the difficulty of maltreatment-related work and the opportunity to develop a professional network that decreases the sense of isolation and risk of professional burnout

For all of its benefits, the multidisciplinary approach is generally considered by child health professionals to be the most effective strategy in dealing with maltreatment investigations. Unfortunately, this effectiveness comes with a price: MDTs are notorious for being labor intensive, difficult to organize, and costly.

CHILD PROTECTIVE SERVICES

CPS, originally referred to as "child welfare," is the agency assigned to receive and investigate cases of suspected child abuse and neglect. CPS is an important function of the county and state government and is guided by principles that preserve the family and ensure each child's physical and emotional safety (**Table 10-1**).

CPS receives many of its reports from ***mandated reporters***, or people of certain professions required by state law to report suspicions of possible child maltreatment in specified circumstances. Of course, mandated reporters are not the only ones who are

Table 10-1. Principles of Child Protective Services	
PRINCIPLE	DESCRIPTION
Safety	All children have the right to live in an environment free from abuse and neglect. The safety of children is the paramount concern that must guide child protection efforts.
Permanency	Children need a family and a permanent place to call home. A sense of continuity and connectedness is central to a child's healthy development.
Child and family well-being	Children deserve nurturing environments in which their physical, emotional, educational, and social needs are met. Child protection practices must take into account each child's needs and should promote healthy development.

Data from Goldman et al.[4]

allowed to make reports: any person may voluntarily make one, regardless of their job. The jobs that are typically labeled as mandated reporters are:

— Physicians, nurses, and other hospital personnel

— Dentists

— Medical examiners

— Coroners

— Mental health professionals

— Social workers

— Teachers, guidance counselors, and other school personnel

— Childcare providers

— Law enforcement officers

In order to encourage reliable and truthful reporting of suspected child maltreatment, most states impose specific penalties upon professionals who fail to comply with their mandated reporting responsibility or who intentionally make false reports. It should be noted that mandated reporters do not have to prove that the maltreatment actually occurred; they simply have to state their reasons for suspecting that it did. In the event that their suspicions are disproved, they will still be protected from civil and criminal liability as long as the report was made in "good faith." This term implies that the reporter is acting upon a genuine suspicion of child maltreatment and not some ulterior motive.

In general, the CPS process consists of 7 essential stages[5]:

1. Intake

2. Initial assessment/investigation

3. Family assessment

4. Case planning

5. Service provision

6. Evaluation of family progress

7. Case closure

Each of these stages are highlighted in **Table 10-2**. CPS often calls upon medical and associated mental health professionals to help determine what steps are in the best interests of each child and family. As the evaluation and investigation move toward developing a treatment plan, another tier of service providers may become involved with the child and family. In-home supports are common, wherein a professional visits the home and provides basic, routine tasks for the child and family. Together, they may cover time management, homework completion, and conflict-resolution strategies. Mental health services might be provided, to bridge the episodic visits to the office. Interface with the education system may also be an important part of the treatment as service plans take shape. School involvement may include early intervention programs, special education, and after-school and recreational enrichment activities.

Ideally, the above care and services should be rendered in a family-centered approach that seeks to empower the family and should incorporate any strengths and abilities the family already has. In addition, services are best delivered in a manner that respects the

Table 10-2. Child Protective Services Process	
CPS STAGE	DESCRIPTION
Intake	Point at which reports of suspected child maltreatment are received by CPS, who must consider 2 issues: — Does the report information meet the legal guidelines for child maltreatment? — How urgent is the required response?

Initial investigation	For cases accepted for investigation, the following questions are asked:
	— Is child maltreatment substantiated as defined by state law?
	— Is the child at risk of maltreatment? If so:
	    — What is the level or risk?
	    — What response will ensure safety?
	    — What care is needed?
	— Does the family have emergency needs that must be met?
	— Should ongoing agency services be offered to the family to reduce the risk or to address the treatment needs of the child?

Family assessment	Comprehensive process for identifying, considering, and weighing factors that affect the child's safety and well-being. Key decisions made as a result of the family assessment include: — What are the family's needs? — What are the effects of maltreatment? — What are the individual's and family's strengths? — How does the family perceive its problems and strengths? — What must change in order for the effects of maltreatment to be reduced or eliminated? — What is the family's motivation and capacity to assure safety, permanency, and well-being?

(continued)

147

Table 10-2. *(continued)*

CPS Stage	Description
Case planning	Comprehensive assessment of the family's circumstances and conditions is the foundation on which the case plan is built. Purposes of case planning are to identify the strategies that will address the effects of maltreatment and lessen the risk of further abuse and neglect. Key decisions made at the case planning stage are: — What are the outcomes that will indicate that risk has been reduced? — What goals must be achieved to reach those outcomes? — What intervention will facilitate the achievement of those outcomes?
Service provision	CPS caseworker arranges for services identified in the plan to help family members achieve the outcomes, goals, and outlined tasks. Each community must provide a broad range of services to meet the many needs of abused and neglected children and their families, including: — Services provided to the entire family (eg, family preservation services, therapy for children and families, family strengthening programs) — Services provided to parents or caregivers (eg, sex offender treatment, parent education, substance abuse treatment, mutual support programs) — Services provided to children (eg, counseling, therapeutic preschool, peer-based training, mentoring programs)
Evaluation of family progress	Monitoring of change should begin as soon as an intervention is implemented and continue throughout the life of a case, with the following questions: — Is the child safe? Have the protective factors, strengths, or safety factors changed, warranting a change or elimination of the existing safety plan or the development of a new safety plan? — What changes, if any, have occurred with respect to the conditions and behaviors contributing to the risk of maltreatment? — What outcomes have been accomplished, and how does the caseworker know that they have been accomplished? — What progress has been made toward achieving case goals? — Have the services been effective in helping clients achieve outcomes and goals? If not, what adjustments need to be made to improve outcomes? — What is the current level of risk in the family? — Have the risk factors been reduced sufficiently so that parents or caregivers can protect their children and meet their developmental needs so the case can be closed? — Has it been determined that reunification is not likely?
Case closure	Point at which the agency no longer maintains an active relationship with the family. The decision to end the agency's involvement must be based on the monitoring and evaluation of the case. Case closure decisions are based on safety and permanency outcomes.

Data from DePanfilis and Salus.[5]

cultural and ethnic diversity of both the family and surrounding community. The perspectives of the various cultural groups that are being served in a given community should be incorporated in the team's deliberations in a substantive way, especially in the area of risk assessment.

In particularly difficult situations in which a child cannot safely remain with his or her family of origin, CPS will place them with substitute caregivers. If the new caregiver is related to the child, it is referred to as *kinship care*; otherwise, it is called *foster care*. The length that a child remains with a substitute caregiver can vary greatly. If the family undergoes changes and is deemed capable of tending to the child's safety and well-being, the child may return to them fairly quickly. However, if the family does not or cannot comply with CPS requirements, the child's new placement can become permanent.

When a child is first placed in substitute care, the primary goal is family reunification. As things progress, the likelihood of success is continually reassessed. It is very important for the substitute caregivers to become involved in the process. They typically become part of the child's extended family and help negotiate relationships that support the goals of both the birth parents and the case plan.

If the substitute care does become permanent, CPS will work with the court system to terminate parental rights and legally free the child for adoption. An increasing focus of CPS is to place each child in a single, permanent location, rather than switching them between several different temporary foster homes. This shift in focus is because the latter option can be psychologically difficult for a child, especially when it happens during critical points in development. Each foster care transition compounds feelings of loss and failing to fit in. The value of permanency to a child's development is becoming increasingly recognized, as is evidenced by the many federal and state laws that are changing to prioritize permanency planning.

Joint Investigations With Law Enforcement

Joint investigations involving both CPS and the police tend to occur in only the most severe and complex cases. The highest number of joint investigations are for cases of suspected sexual abuse.[6] CPS agencies report that approximately 20% of their child maltreatment investigations are jointly conducted, and law enforcement agencies report that 80% to 95% of their maltreatment investigations are jointly conducted.[6] Part of the reason for this collaboration is that sexual abuse cases usually lack medical evidence and objective witnesses, so an increased number of resources are needed to run an effective investigation.[7] Suspected sexual abuse investigations also require a number of time-consuming interviews, that require a fair amount of prior training to complete properly. Contrast this with physical abuse and neglect cases, which often have obvious physical evidence and are frequently seen by investigators as more straightforward. Approximately 42% of cases jointly investigated by CPS and the police are substantiated.[6]

During joint investigations between the police and CPS, the police typically assume the following key roles and responsibilities:

— Conducting the criminal component of the child maltreatment investigations, including:

    — Interviewing the victims, caregivers, witnesses, and suspected perpetrators

    — Gathering physical evidence at the suspected crime scene and any other evidence that is turned over to them during the investigation

— Arresting suspected perpetrators

— Working with the prosecutor to determine if enough evidence exists to bring criminal charges against the suspected perpetrator

— Assisting with the protection of the child

— Providing protection to CPS staff if confrontation occurs with alleged offenders

— Supporting the child and family through the criminal investigation process and during court proceedings (**Figure 10-1**)

MENTAL HEALTH ISSUES

Mental health—or, as it is now frequently called, behavioral health—service providers (psychiatrists, psychologists, and other mental health professionals) assist parents during the initial CPS evaluation and provide treatment once CPS investigation and treatment planning end. Mental health professionals are a vital component of the interdisciplinary approach to the evaluation and treatment of child abuse, largely because of their roles in ameliorating the short- and long-term impacts of maltreatment. Mental health professionals dealing with child maltreatment issues have specific responsibilities:

— Identifying and reporting suspected cases of child maltreatment

— Conducting evaluations of abused and neglected children and their families

— Providing treatment for abused and neglected children and their families

— Providing clinical consultation to CPS during the assessment, treatment planning, and treatment implementation

— Providing expert testimony to the court when necessary

— Organizing and facilitating self-help groups for caregivers who are at risk of maltreating (secondary prevention) or who have already abused or neglected their children (tertiary prevention)

— Participating on MDTs focused on child maltreatment issues

PSYCHOLOGICAL CONSEQUENCES OF ABUSE OR NEGLECT ON CHILDREN

Because no children respond to maltreatment in the same way, professional discussions of its psychological and emotional clinical consequences tend to be framed in terms of ranges of response. Such ranges, or "spectrums," can be confusing but are the most accurate way of discussing the mental health implications of child abuse and neglect.[8] For example, on the "internalizing versus externalizing" range of responses, some children internalize their symptoms and appear socially withdrawn, while some children externalize their symptoms and aggressively "act out." Fully externalizing or internalizing are opposites in this range of responses, and most children's actual responses fall somewhere in the middle.

Despite the lack of specific, predictable responses, the overwhelming majority of the research on the mental health consequences of child maltreatment does in fact support a view that responses are best explained and understood as reactions to general traumatization.[9] Several doctors looked at published research on the effects of child sexual abuse, focusing on 37 studies published over 15 years.[10] They found clear evidence of a link between child sexual abuse and a defined set of negative short- and long-term effects, including posttraumatic stress disorder (PTSD), depression, suicide, sexual promiscuity, the victim-perpetrator cycle, and poor academic performance. Even though each child will respond differently, it is clear that maltreatment has great

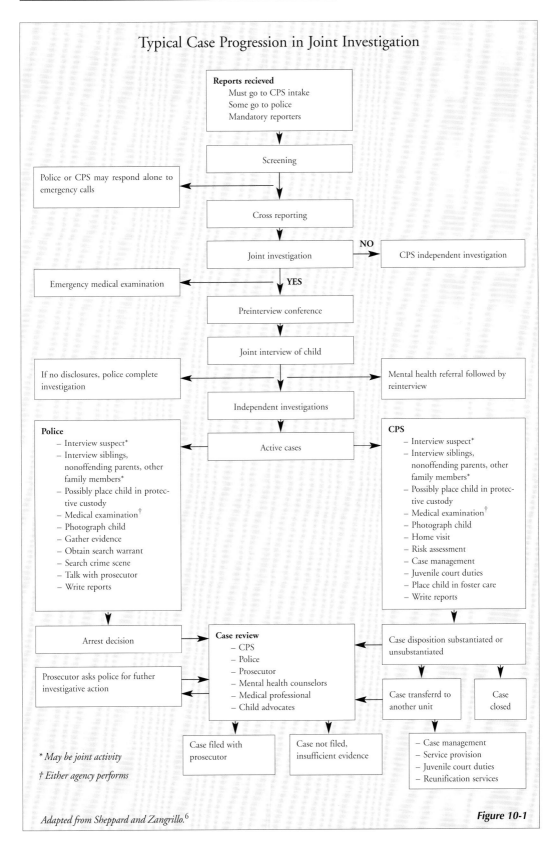

Typical Case Progression in Joint Investigation

Reports recieved
    Must go to CPS intake
    Some go to police
    Mandatory reporters

↓

Screening

Police or CPS may respond alone to emergency calls ←

↓

Cross reporting

↓

Joint investigation — **NO** → CPS independent investigation

YES ↓

Emergency medical examination ←

Preinterview conference

↓

Joint interview of child

If no disclosures, police complete investigation ←   → Mental health referral followed by reinterview

↓

Independent investigations

↓

Police
– Interview suspect*
– Interview siblings, nonoffending parents, other family members*
– Possibly place child in protective custody
– Medical examination†
– Photograph child
– Gather evidence
– Obtain search warrant
– Search crime scene
– Talk with prosecutor
– Write reports

Active cases

CPS
– Interview suspect*
– Interview siblings, nonoffending parents, other family members*
– Possibly place child in protective custody
– Medical examination†
– Photograph child
– Home visit
– Risk assessment
– Case management
– Juvenile court duties
– Place child in foster care
– Write reports

↓

Arrest decision →

Case review
– CPS
– Police
– Prosecutor
– Mental health counselors
– Medical professional
– Child advocates

← Case disposition substantiated or unsubstantiated

Prosecutor asks police for futher investigative action →

← Case transferrd to another unit   Case closed

↓   ↓

Case filed with prosecutor   Case not filed, insufficient evidence

– Case management
– Service provision
– Juvenile court duties
– Reunification services

* May be joint activity

† Either agency performs

Adapted from Sheppard and Zangrillo.[6]

Figure 10-1

potential to damage a child's emotional and psychological well-being, and its treatment needs the assistance of mental health professionals.

Mental Health Interventions

Step One: The Caregiver and the Home and School Environments

Promoting the best possible mental and behavioral health in maltreated children starts with addressing the caregivers' and the child's home and moves to getting help from professionals in the psychiatric and psychological fields. Caregivers working toward promoting the best possible mental or behavioral health for the children in their care should focus on creating a supportive home environment. A supportive home environment allows and encourages children to disclose their concerns and feelings openly, and an important characteristic of this environment is an atmosphere of mutual trust, respect, honesty, and openness between caregivers and children. The key to building this atmosphere is communication. Note that true communication involves more than just talking, teaching, and explaining. To be really effective, it must also include listening.

Maintaining a normal, daily routine is fundamental to creating a supportive environment. Children who have been victimized need more than ever a consistency in family rules, limits, discipline, school, and entertainment. Caregivers should not forget the health-promoting value of fun outings such as family trips to the mall or the movie theater. In addition, as discussed in Chapter 7, Schools and Child Abuse, enlisting schools' support in the healing process by discussing a child's unique needs with teachers and making sure the school is part of the treatment plan is also likely to be helpful.

Creating a supportive home environment may also require seeking the assistance of professionals who can assist with counseling and follow-up care for both parents and children. Disclosure of any kind of abuse creates stress for the entire family. Families may need to seek professional help in order to effectively deal with the complex set of circumstances involved in child maltreatment cases.

Caregivers frequently feel overwhelmed by the confusion and the many other emotions associated with the disclosed situation. Such reactions are normal. Caregivers should seek out friends, family members, religious clergy, or others who can serve as an emotional support system. However, do not expect immediate results. Healing takes time, and time does allow for healing. The word *crisis*, by definition, refers to a situation that, though troubling, is also temporary. Eventually, normalcy will reappear. That said, time working by itself is not always enough. Complete recovery may also depend on professional counseling. A pediatrician, local child protection agency, or a mental health facility will be able to provide appropriate referrals.

Step Two: Professional Help

Significant advancements have been made since the 1980s in terms of health professionals' understanding of how best to help children and their families deal with the trauma of maltreatment. Of course, each situation is different, and each child's and family's response is different as well. There is no one approach that will be effective every time. However, some basic approaches have emerged in terms of what is most likely to be helpful to children who have been maltreated.

Children are in a constant state of development physically, cognitively, emotionally, and psychologically. As such, the techniques mental health professionals use and the ways they will be able to help children will vary with each child's age and development. However, regardless of where a child is developmentally, children in general do best in caregiving environments that have a sufficient amount of stability and consistency to create a foundation upon which their changing needs can effectively be met. As a supplement to a supportive environment, professionals can help caregivers in addressing the trauma experience that comes from child maltreatment.

Chapter 11 presents art therapy as an ideal approach for helping children express their feelings and emotional responses in a nonverbal manner. Specifically, art therapy allows children to use symbolic language to communicate how they are feeling, since making art is often easier than talking. Play therapy works similarly: Allowing children to express how they are feeling using toys can be a more comfortable way than coming up with specific words to identify emotions. Art therapy and play therapy, when facilitated by skilled professionals, can open the lines of communication for children of various ages, developmental levels, and cognitive/verbal capabilities.

More traditional forms of therapy may also be effective. Individual, group, and family therapy may potentially have a role to play in helping children and families come to terms with the traumatization associated with child maltreatment. Dr. William Friedrich, a leader in the field of developmental psychology, has provided a simple but comprehensive model that assists in discussing how to think of professional psychological help for children and families. In this model, 3 organizing principles—attachment, self-control (or self-regulation), and self-perception—can be used to understand the mental and behavioral health issues that may need attention in cases of child abuse and neglect.[11]

Attachment
Attachment, the first organizing principle in Friedrich's model, is both biological and psychological and describes the ability to form mutually supportive relationships. Therefore, being victimized by a caregiver might affect a child's ability to bond with others, especially if the victimization occurs early in development, when dependence on one's caregivers is at its highest.[11] Dr. Friedrich describes different types of attachment, ranging from secure—the healthiest form—to several dysfunctional forms that are not supportive of a child's sense of security and, if present, need professional attention. Individual and group therapy for attachment problems address forming connections to others, learning how to feel safe with others, and learning how to develop a sense of empathy. Family therapy can then work on helping the whole family set goals for healthy attachment formation and helping the child, who is having difficulty feeling connected and cared for, feel more supported in the given environment.

Self-Control
Self-control, the second principle, addresses maltreated children's sense of being out of control. The abusive or neglectful environment is full of stress, unpredictability, and chaos. As a result of being exposed to a high degree of unpredictability, children may develop a wide range of dysfunctional behaviors and responses to everyday situations. Individual and group therapy typically treat the anxiety, stress management, and self-calming issues that are likely to be pertinent to children dealing with this set of problems. Family therapy might help the family work on setting routines, being more predictable, and decreasing the amount of routine stress present in the caregiving environment.

Self-Perception
Self-perception, the third and final principle, deals with the way children see themselves. After being maltreated, children often view themselves poorly. Dr. Suzanne Sgroi and colleagues have described this as having a sense of being "damaged goods."[12] Individual and group therapy would seek to adjust their perceptions, create an understanding of their inherent value and worth, and shift blame for the abuse from the self

to the perpetrator. Family therapy could then help the family develop an approach to dealing with the children and their interactions, with the focus on being encouraging, nurturing, supportive, and positive within the home.

These 3 principles are applicable to children of all ages. However, with the onset of adolescence, psychological issues may become more complex as teenagers balance their dependence on caregivers with their desires to be independent. Thus, though adolescents may be in need of help, they are inclined to resist help and see it as a further encroachment on their independence. Additionally, a history of sexual abuse may complicate adolescents' growing sense and understanding of their own sexuality and add another dimension to an already challenging set of clinical issues.

WHAT TO DO WHEN NO SERVICES EXIST WITHIN A COMMUNITY

This chapter has already discussed team approaches, which foster professional collaboration in dealing with child abuse and neglect, as the ideal way of serving children and families. Communities, however, may not have a full range of services available to deal with cases of child abuse and neglect, or professionals may not be comfortable with the existing maltreatment programs in a given geographical area. In these situations, professionals and community members interested in helping children and families must see the opportunity that exists to design and implement a set of necessary services for children and caregivers. A number of challenges will inevitably rise during the formation of these services. However, they can be overcome with hard work and perseverance. The starting point for building such a team should be a focus on the needs of the community's children and families. The following specific steps have been suggested[3]:

— Identify members who are committed to a team approach and who are supported by their agency/employer to participate in the interdisciplinary approach.

— Hold an initial meeting in which members share previous experiences with child maltreatment and teamwork.

— Develop a mission statement that addresses the team's purpose, scope of activities, and guiding principles, all of which should be discussed and agreed upon.

— Create standards and written protocols to specify the cases to be considered, the responsibility of each professional and agency, and the agreed-upon procedures for different aspects of the case.

For the team to be successful, participants and participating agencies need to pay consistent attention to internal conflict resolution practices. An MDT requires an environment of mutual respect that recognizes both the complexity of working with child sexual abuse cases and the valuable contribution that each professional and organization makes for the team to function well.

Over the decades, professional experience has consistently pointed to the benefits of joint investigations that help coordinate community resources directed at evaluating and treating children and families. Fostering teamwork may be difficult, but the benefits that children, families, and professionals accrue are well worth the effort and commitment that an effective MDT requires.

CONCLUSION

Child abuse and neglect is a problem that requires a team of professionals to work together on behalf of a child and family with a goal of promoting the most healthy development possible for the maltreated child. CPS and police have the responsibility to investigate and intervene once child maltreatment has been reported. CPS works to design a care plan that meets children's needs for a safe and nurturing family environment. Experiencing the trauma of being maltreated is likely to have a dramatic, negative impact on children. Although no standard response to maltreatment has been identified among children, most professionals agree that significant mental and behavioral impacts are likely. Attention to maltreated children's psychological well-being begins with caregivers creating a supportive caregiving environment and possibly involves professional mental health experts as well. Ultimately, the destructive world to which maltreated children are accustomed needs to be replaced with a caring, supportive environment in which they are valued and cared for in a nurturing, predictable, and loving manner.

REFERENCES

1. US Department of Health & Human Services. *Child Maltreatment 2004*. Washington, DC: US Dept of Health and Human Services; 2006. Available at: http://www.acf.hhs.gov/programs/cb/pubs/cm04/index.htm. Accessed June 28, 2006.

2. O'Neil EH. *Health Professions Education for the Future: Schools in Service to the Nations*. San Francisco, Calif: Pew Health Professions Commission; 1993.

3. Ells M. *Forming a Multidisciplinary Team to Investigate Child Abuse: A Portable Guide to Investigating Child Abuse*. Washington, DC: US Dept of Justice; 1998.

4. Goldman J, Salus MK, Wolcott D, Kennedy KY. *A Coordinated Response to Child Abuse and Neglect: The Foundation for Practice*. Washington, DC: US Dept of Health and Human Services; 2003. Child Abuse and Neglect User Manual Series.

5. DePanfilis D, Salus MK. *Child Protective Services: A Guide for Caseworkers*. Washington, DC: US Dept of Health and Human Services; 2003. Child Abuse and Neglect User Manual Series.

6. Sheppard DI, Zangrillo PA. Coordinating investigations of child abuse. *Public Welf.* 1996;54:21-31.

7. Pence D, Wilson C. *Team Investigation of Child Sexual Abuse: The Uneasy Alliance*. Thousand Oaks, Calif: Sage Publications; 1994.

8. Berliner L, Elliott DM. Sexual abuse of children. In: Briere J, Berliner L, Bulkley J, Jenny C, Reid T, eds. *The APSAC Handbook on Child Maltreatment*. Thousand Oaks, Calif: Sage Publications; 1996.

9. Kendall-Tackett K, Williams L, Finkelhor D. Impact of sexual abuse on children: a review and synthesis of recent empirical studies. *Psychol Bull.* 1993;113:164-180.

10. Paolucci EO, Genuis ML, Violato C. A meta-analysis of the published research on the effects of child sexual abuse. *J Psychol.* 2001;135:17-36.

11. Friedrich WN. An integrated model of psychotherapy for abused children. In: Myers JEB, Berliner L, Briere J, Hendrix CT, Jenny C, Reid TA, eds. *The APSAC Handbook on Child Maltreatment*. 2nd ed. Thousand Oaks, Calif: Sage Publications; 2002:139-157.

12. Sgroi SM, Blick LC, Porter FS. A conceptual framework for child sexual abuse. In: Sgroi SM, ed. *Handbook of Clinical Intervention in Child Sexual Abuse*. Lexington, Mass: Lexington; 1998:9-37.

Chapter 11

ART THERAPY

Elizabeth A. Warson, MA, ATR-BC, LPC, NCC
Kay Stovall, MA, ATR-BC, MFT

Art therapists often encounter children and adults who exclaim that they cannot draw. One reply might be, "You were probably drawing long before you were writing." Art is a symbolic language, and, for children, making art is often easier than talking about how they are feeling and what they are thinking. This is an important concept in terms of communicating with them; children do communicate better through art. This nonverbal form of communication is essentially an outlet for expression of feeling. Art therapy can be especially helpful in cases of child abuse or neglect because children—especially young children—lack the vocabulary to discuss their experience and emotions.

WHAT IS ART THERAPY?

Creating art does not always serve this purpose, but it can, under the right conditions, be therapeutic and life enhancing. Counselors, psychiatrists, and psychotherapists have incorporated art into their practice for decades and know the benefit of nonverbal expression. Art therapists are specifically trained to understand and use the art process therapeutically. "Because art therapy permits expression of feelings and thoughts in a manner that is often less threatening than strictly verbal means, there is a level of comfort and a sense of safety sometimes not found in traditional therapy alone."[1]

CHILDREN'S ART DEVELOPMENT

Developmental milestones are apparent in children's artwork. Parents often inquire about what is normal, abnormal, or even exceptional in their child's art productions. As with learning to walk and talk in infancy, there is a developmental range in artistic ability, and within that range one can observe growth. Scribbling is the earliest stage of drawing (ages 2 to 3 years), when children depict an array of scribbles from random lines to the beginnings of circles. Eventually, children name their scribbles, indicating their desire for the marks to represent something[2] (**Figures 11-1-a, b, c, d,** and **e**).

Have you ever wondered why children draw people with arms coming out of their head? This is called a "tadpole figure," and it is typical of children aged 4 to 6 years. A

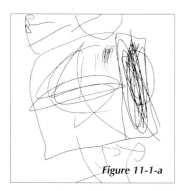

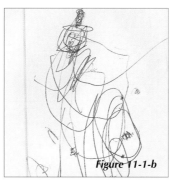

Figure 11-1-a

Figure 11-1-b

Figure 11-1-a and **b**. *2 year old. Example showing process of discovering and experimenting with the basic scribble shapes that will be the basis for all other artwork and writing.*

Figure 11-1-c

Figure 11-1-d

Figure 11-1-e

Figure 11-1-c. 3 year old experiments with the basic scribble shapes and uses scribble lines and circles to form letters and words (Mom, Dad).

Figure 11-1-d. 3 year old. "It's raining on the ground."

Figure 11-1-e. 4 year old. Scribbles.

tadpole figure represents an emerging concept of a person. During this early stage of drawing, children use color in a personalized way—trees can be purple because purple happens to be their favorite color—and themes are often close to home, meaning family, house, pets, and favorite activities. Content, figures, and preferences in terms of art supplies constantly change, reflecting children's developing minds (**Figures 11-2-a, b, c, d,** and **e**). A 5 year old will have a different story about a single piece of art each time someone asks.

Table 11-1 illustrates some of the many materials that children may become enthusiastic about at various times in their artistic development.

As children develop, their concept of space, perspective, use of color, and inclusion of detail becomes more advanced[2] (**Figures 11-3-a, b, c,** and **d; 11-4-a, b,** and **c;** and **11-5-a, b, c,** and **d**). The stages in art are not fixed, and children often move between them. Parents can observe growth and development through artwork, but each child experiences these stages in his or her own time. What is important is that there is a developmental progression. Parents are often eager to know how their child rates in terms of artistic development, and the best way to do this is to keep a collection of their child's artwork to measure growth and change. Forget about rating individual works and focus instead on progression.

Art reflects various stages in our lives and our inner feelings and ideas, making art potentially therapeutic. The series of drawings shown in **Figures 11-6-a, b, c,** and **d** were done in a 15-minute period of time by a 5-year-old boy who came to his therapy session extremely upset and angry. The only words he said when he arrived were "No" and "You can't make me." This language is typical of a 2 year old who is trying to deal with difficult feelings. After the boy had a temper tantrum and drew these pictures, he was able to regain his composure, talk about what was bothering him, and leave the session feeling relaxed.

Figure 11-2-a. 4 year old. Blending scribbles, lines, and shapes to draw a person.

Figure 11-2-b. 4 year old. Human figure with a circle used for the head and lines for the arms and legs.

Figure 11-2-a

Figure 11-2-b

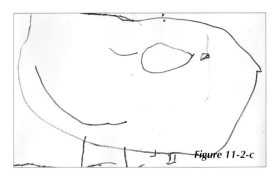

Figure 11-2-c

Figure 11-2-c. 4 year old. "My friend Emily."

Figure 11-2-d. 6 year old. "A Happy Animal."

Figure 11-2-e. 7 year old. "My Home in the Snow."

Figure 11-2-d

Figure 11-2-e

Table 11-1. Art Materials

Papers	**Craft Objects**
Construction paper	Clay
Tissue paper	Pipe cleaners
Used wrapping paper	String (thread, yarn, twine)
Old wallpaper books	Popsicle sticks
Old holiday cards	Buttons
Magazines and catalogs	Beans
Newspapers	Beads
Writing/Drawing Utensils	Nuts and bolts
	Paper towel or toilet paper rolls
Pencils	Boxes
Pens	Fabrics
Colored pencils	Stickers
Markers	Canvas
Crayons (water, plastic, oil, regular)	Small tree branches
Pastels	Foam shapes
Charcoal	Shoulder pads
Paints	**Other**
Water colors	Scissors
Tempera paints	Rulers
Finger paints	Tape of all sizes and shapes
Water color pencils	Glues of all colors and styles
Spray paint	Rubber bands
Food coloring	Templates
Paint brushes	Flour and water
Sponges	

Adapted from Rickert.[3]

Figure 11-3-b

Figure 11-3-a

Figure 11-3-c

Figure 11-3-a. *7 year old. "Mom and Dad's Chairs." The basic scribble, shapes, and lines are evolving into more defined objects and numbers.*

Figure 11-3-b. *8 year old. "Visitation."*

Figure 11-3-c. *8 year old. "Mandala." Basic scribble lines have become symbols of geometric lines. The child's self-assurance and definite ways of looking at things emerge, as shown by the full-bodied colors and distinctive lines.*

Figure 11-3-d. *9 year old. "Camping Sunset." An awareness of the environment and how things fit together are shown in this drawing.*

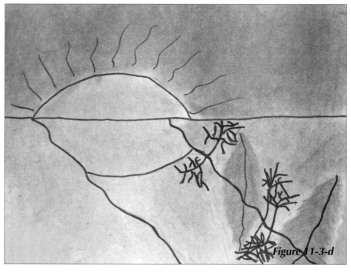

Figure 11-3-d

Figure 11-4-a

Figure 11-4-b

Figure 11-4-a. *9 year old. "Racoon." Basic scribble lines and circles have evolved into tools that can be used to emphasize details and try to be more realistic.*

Figure 11-4-b. *10 year old. "Bamboo Watercolor." Even while experimenting with watercolors, this child's artwork reflects a realistic depiction of bamboo. Basic scribble lines are part of the artwork, serving as natural markings to depict a lifelike image.*

Figure 11-4-c. *11 year old. "Me." The artist's need to reflect herself and her gender can be seen in this mask. Decorations appear for the first time at this age.*

Figure 11-4-c

161

Figure 11-5-a

Figure 11-5-b

Figure 11-5-c

Figure 11-5-d

Figure 11-5-a. *17 year old. "Willy." Note the development and exaggeration of detail.*

Figure 11-5-b. *16 year old. "Christ." This is a subjective drawing of how this figure "feels" to the artist. Note the shading and the attempt to create a definite expression on the face. Basic scribble lines and shapes are completely evolved as tools to create an image with a purposeful intent, interpretation, and feeling.*

Figure 11-5-c. *13 year old. "Still Life." Pseudonaturalistic drawing. There is greater attention to detail and objects that have a personal meaning.*

Figure 11-5-d. *14 year old. "Winnie the Pooh." Pseudonaturalisic drawing. Cartooning is common at this age.*

Figure 11-6-a

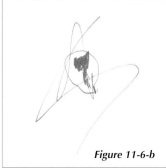

Figure 11-6-b

Figure 11-6-d

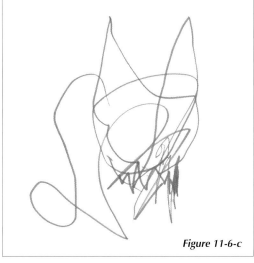

Figure 11-6-c

Figure 11-6-a. *"A Scribble." This is typical of a 2 year old. After this, the child grabbed a piece of paper and crunched it after promising he would draw a picture, another behavior very typical of a 2 year old.*

Figure 11-6-b. *"Another Scribble." This scribble is smaller and has a circle in the middle with more shaded area. This is more typical of a child moving into the next developmental stage, ages 4 to 7 years.*

Figure 11-6-c. *"More Scribbles." This drawing is more open and almost appears to take on a shape. The basic scribbles, lines, and circles are more organized than in the earlier 2 drawings.*

Figure 11-6-d. *"The Volcano in Me." The child had calmed himself and began putting his energy into the drawing. Although the organization is not perfect, the picture shows that the child's perspective and self-control are greatly improved. This is a picture of the volcano inside him that explodes. There are 4 trees firmly planted in the ground. This is much more age-appropriate for a 5 year old.*

When a child is abused, the abuse affects his or her creative development, making it difficult for him or her to move through the various developmental stages correctly. Often, children become stuck at the stage where the abuse occurred, or they may regress consistently to that age when they express themselves in artwork. Creative development flows from stage to stage in children who are well-treated; they are always moving toward a more complete and mature expression of themselves. When victims of maltreatment try to create, they create from what they see, who they are, and where they have been, all of which are based on injury rather than good health. Children who are not mistreated and can explore their mental, emotional, physical, and spiritual selves without fear, learning to feel comfortable with themselves and where they fit in the world. Children who have to repress pain, anger, and other negative feelings in order to survive are using their energy to protect and defend themselves. Their efforts to cope with stress are reflected in their art.

WHAT IS "NORMAL"?

Knowing that there is a developmental course to art making and an approach to discussing and observing art productions is vital before making assumptions about what is or is not "normal." Parents and mental health professionals alike have sought a checklist of graphic indicators related to sexual abuse, incest, and other forms of trauma. However, this checklist does not exist, and for good reason: One cannot assign meaning to individual features or omissions.[4] As a result, it is necessary to be cautious when looking at children's artwork for indications of trauma and abuse, as the art productions alone cannot be used as evidence for abuse.[5] Parents are often most qualified to identify these indications in their children's artwork and know when to seek help because they are most familiar with their child's skill level. Professionals such as art therapists can be especially helpful in understanding the artwork and making inferences about children's art productions.

TALKING TO CHILDREN ABOUT THEIR ART

Parents who have ever had the urge to say, "What's that?" to a piece of their child's art might want to rethink their approach. Considering the tremendous variation in children's drawings, parents are advised to approach discussing the artwork with fewer preconceptions. Dr. Schirrmacher recommends moving away from more traditional responses to an alternate approach that encourages communication.[6] He states that adults tend to rely on complimenting ("It's beautiful"), expressing judgment ("Good," "Great"), assigning value ("I like it"), questioning ("What is it?"), and overly probing ("Tell me all about it"). Alternate approaches that seem to be more effective focus on fewer adult intrusions and place less emphasis on skill.[5] To engage in an effective dialogue, first pause and reflect to avoid making an impulsive comment. Comment about the artistic elements after becoming familiar with the basics in terms of line, shape, colors, patterns, textures, and space. These are formal qualities in art that children are becoming aware of. Focusing on formal qualities is especially helpful for discussing nonrepresentational or abstract art. Children can and do make abstract art; it is fun for them—a physical and emotional release. Helpful comments such as "I see you used thick blue lines across your paper" and "You created a rounded, hollow form" can be more encouraging and prompt the child to talk more about the picture. Do not rule out the possibility of asking for a story, because children often have associations that give meaning to their artwork.

Approaches to discussing representational or nonabstract art are somewhat similar; however, Schirrmacher suggests that because the symbols are often apparent, one should refer to them as such rather than how they look. For example, refer to "the sun" instead of "a yellow circle with radiating lines."[6] One could also comment about what impressions the artwork creates, for instance: "It looks like the sun is trying to peek through the cloud," or, "The sun and cloud on the right balance the smoking chimney on the left."[6] More meaningful dialogue will often develop out of an initial comment like these and can consist of a brief interchange, making certain that it does not become an "interrogation."

FINDING OUT WHAT IS WRONG

Sometimes parents have the uncomfortable feeling that something is bothering their child or that something has happened though the child either cannot or has not mentioned any particular problem. If, over time, a child produces a significant number of drawings that make his or her parents uneasy, or if his or her responses to questions about the art seem strange, the child may be in need of help.

The drawings shown in **Figures 11-7-a, b, c, d, e, f,** and **g** are part of a series brought in by a parent who became concerned about some of the changes that seemed to be emerging in the child's artwork. The child created them in and out of school over a 5-month period; some represented subjects assigned by the teacher, and others were spontaneous creations. Drawings that the child had done previously did not have sad faces, and the outside scenes tended to have people and children in them, whereas the ones in this array have an "emptiness" to them. The parent was concerned that the child was experiencing too much family-related stress and may have been expressing this feeling in the drawings represented. Despite the child's ability to create artwork that accurately expressed feelings and trauma related to the situation, it was not until much later that the child was able to talk about the stress.

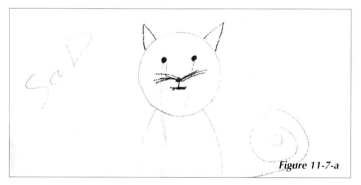

Figure 11-7-a. "A Sad Cat."

Figure 11-7-b. "An Empty Bench."

Figure 11-7-c. "My Home."

Figure 11-7-a

Figure 11-7-b

Figure 11-7-c

Figure 11-7-d

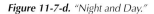

Figure 11-7-e

Figure 11-7-f

Figure 11-7-g

Figure 11-7-d. *"Night and Day."*

Figure 11-7-e. *"Coloring Book Page."*

Figure 11-7-f. *"Bangeled Tiger."*

Figure 11-7-g. *"Watercolor of House."*

ART THERAPY CASE EXAMPLES
ADJUSTING TO A NEW SIBLING

Figure 11-8 was created by a very intelligent, first-born, 4-year-old girl. The arrival of a newborn in the home brought out the following reactions:

— Loud objection to any visitors to the home

— Remarks about who was actually going to be the infant's mother, indicating competitiveness

— Deviations from traditional drawing style

This drawing sums up the child's feelings about the new sibling. The mother is shown in the upper left and the older sibling is below her, lying down like an infant. The newborn is drawn on the right as a large figure with 4 mouths. When the girl was asked about the picture, she said, "That's just how he is!" By seeing that the older child felt stressed and confused by the infant, the parents were able to adjust the way they interacted with her and help ease her transition to sharing her parents with the new sibling.

Adjusting to a New Stepparent

Even under the best of circumstances, marriage is challenging. Remarriage can intensify the challenge, and remarriages involving children can sometimes feel like a military war game. Knowing of these difficulties, a mother brought one of her children to a therapist so she could discuss her feelings about her mother's upcoming remarriage.

During the session, the therapist suggested drawing what the family was like now (**Figure 11-9-a**) and what she thought would happen once a stepfather joined the house (**Figure 11-9-b**). In **Figure 11-9-a**, the youngest child is watching television, the child who made the drawing is getting ready to ride her bike and play, and the oldest child is drawn as the star of the family. On the far left, the mother is shown with a question mark over her head, indicating that she is confused. The people in the drawing are full figures and all 4 have smiles on their faces. In **Figure 11-9-b**, the youngest child is still watching television. The oldest child has disappeared and only quotation marks remain around the space where the oldest child was in the first drawing. The mother is on the far right, standing behind the child who drew the picture and is yelling at her. The child has drawn herself standing in front of the stepfather, who is tied up to a chair and gagged, pointing at him and laughing. All of the original family members are drawn much thinner or gone, except the youngest child.

The potential stepparent did not want to intrude on this family and remained quiet. Through the therapy, it was discovered that the child interpreted this soft and passive behavior as weakness; she was concerned that "another marriage would be ruined

Figure 11-8

Figure 11-9-b

Figure 11-8. Drawn by a child dealing with the arrival of a new sibling.

Figure 11-9-a. Drawing of how the family is now

Figure 11-9-b. Drawing of how the family would be if the stepfather moved in.

Figure 11-9-a

Figure 11-10

Figure 11-10. Sand tray box.

Figure 11-11-a. Drawing showing child's "bad" side.

Figure 11-11-b. Drawing showing child's "good" side.

because of the fighting." Art therapy helped give the engaged couple a clear picture of what was bothering the child. They were then able to address the problem and plan for how authority issues could be approached.

HEALING FROM ABUSE

Figure 11-10 is a sand tray box from a session with a 6-year-old boy ("Sam") who was sexually abused by his older adolescent brother. Because of Sam's interest in building and construction methods, Sam and his art therapist created a clay family, even including family pets. Over time, Sam was able to reenact traumatic experiences through therapeutic play. This provided him with a safe and contained way to play out real and pretend scenarios in the sand box, allowing him to ultimately express how he felt responsible for the abuse that occurred and the subsequent breakup of the family. Through this process of art and play therapy, Sam was able to verbally express ideas that, in his mind, he was forbidden to say. With the support of his parents and art therapist, he was able to symbolically create a new concept of family through a pretend home.

The child who drew **Figures 11-11-a** and **b** had experienced several physical and psychological episodes of abuse, both personally and as a witness. He was brought to the art therapist for help in the healing process. When he was asked about himself, he said he was "good and bad." He was asked to draw a picture showing "his good" and "his bad." **Figure 11-11-a** shows his "bad"side, represented by a devil figure. **Figure 11-11-b** shows his "good" side, represented by an angel. The proportions of the figures accurately reflected his feelings about himself. This child also drew his good part on the back of the paper with his bad part. He said that he did this because it reflected how he was: "I put the bad side on top where people see it in case I have to fight with them. I don't show the good side because they'd just cream me!" Part of the therapy focused on helping him balance his "good and bad" more evenly with both on top so that people could see the good side as well as the bad.

Figure 11-11-a

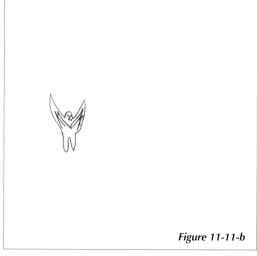

Figure 11-11-b

DEALING WITH THE PAST

Anger is often a response to dealing with traumatic events. However, the ways in which anger can be expressed depend in part on cultural, religious, and familial values. "Maria," a 15-year-old Native American girl, illustrated the development of her concept of anger from a self-portrait in a marker drawing (**Figure 11-12-a**), a paper mask, and a stylized clay sculpture (**Figure 11-12-b**). This method of externalizing her anger allowed her to safely express strong feelings that Native American youths find difficult to assert because of their cultural upbringing.[7]

Figure 11-12-a

Children who have been abused in the past often are in need of additional counseling as they grow older. This was the case with "Steve," a 16-year-old boy who was repeatedly sexually abused as a young child by his stepfather. Steve participated in a grief and loss group and, through the support of his peers and the art therapist, was able to depict and write a detailed account of anticipating his stepfather walking down a "long, dark hallway" (**Figure 11-13-a**) headed toward his room, where he lay motionless and helpless. As an adolescent, this experience still haunted Steve in his dreams, and he would reportedly barricade his door in his sleep. The grief and loss group enabled him to work through these traumatic memories and express his feelings of grief, which are depicted in his layered paper collage (**Figure 11-13-b**).

Figure 11-12-b

CONCLUSION

Artwork can help a child express the need for help, and some children learn through art therapy how to better express their feelings (**Figures 11-14-a, b,** and **c**). Parents are encouraged to pay attention to intuition, that feeling that tells them when something may be wrong. Also pay attention when a child produces a significant amount of disturbing artwork over a long period of time. Parents who believe consultation with an art therapist would be helpful can locate a professional in their area on the Art Therapist Locator Web site (http://arttherapistlocator.org) or contact the American Art Therapy Association.

Figure 11-12-a. Self-portrait drawing depicting anger.

Figure 11-12-b. Self-portrait clay sculpture depicting anger.

Figure 11-13-a. Drawing of dark hallway.

Figure 11-13-b. Layered paper collage depicting grief.

Figure 11-13-a

Figure 11-13-b

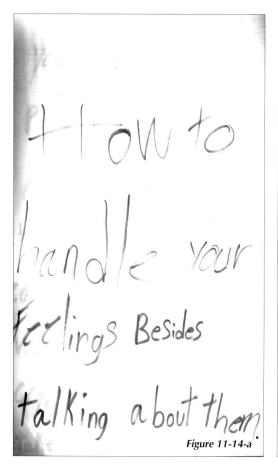

How to handle your feelings Besides talking about them

Figure 11-14-a

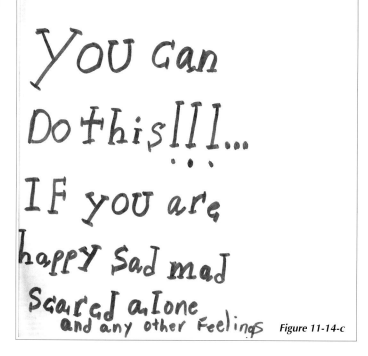

You can Draw, Play the Piano, right a Story, exercise, Do Somthing well, listen to music, cook somthing, Go for a walk, take a Drive, cry, Do Art, Beat a pillow, take a Bath or a shower.

Figure 11-14-b

Figure 11-14-a, b and **c.** Pages from a child telling how to handle feelings.

You can Do this!!!... IF you are happy Sad mad Scared alone and any other Feelings

Figure 11-14-c

REFERENCES

1. Malchiodi C, ed. *Handbook of Art Therapy*. New York, NY: Guildford; 2003.

2. Lowenfeld V, Brittain WL. *Creative and Mental Growth*. 8th ed. New York, NY: Macmillan; 1987.

3. Rickert CM. Art therapy. In: Monteleone JA. *A Parent's & Teacher's Handbook on Identifying and Preventing Child Abuse*. St. Louis, Mo: GW Medical Publishing; 1998:175-192.

4. Malchiodi C. *Breaking the Silence: Art Therapy With Children From Violent Homes*. 2nd ed. Bristol, Pa: Brunner/Mazel; 1997.

5. Haygood MM. Diagnosis or dilemma: drawings of sexually abused children. *Art Ther: J Am Art Ther Assoc*. 1994;11:37-42.

6. Schirrmacher R. Talking with young children about their art. *Young Child*. 1986;41:3-7.

7. Sue DW, Sue D. *Counseling the Culturally Different: Theory and Practice*. 3rd ed. New York, NY: John Wiley; 1999.

Chapter 12

PREVENTION EFFORTS: THE NEXT CHALLENGE

Peggy S. Pearl, EdD
Angelo P. Giardino, MD, PhD, MPH, FAAP

Preventing child abuse and neglect before it begins is a goal many share. In health care and social services, child maltreatment prevention efforts include a wide variety of activities, initiatives, and programs aimed at reducing risk and harm to children. Public education, legislative action, and effective programming are all ways to deliver services to children who are affected or at risk. Prevention efforts have already been highly successful in other fields: Since the 1980s, they have been responsible for dramatically reducing the rates of alcohol-related traffic deaths, mother-to-child HIV/AIDS transmission, and adolescent pregnancies.[1] The success that prevention efforts have yielded for these public health issues has inspired health care and social services professionals to work more toward prevention as well, hoping to see comparably dramatic reductions to the rates of child abuse and neglect.

In order to make this reduction in child abuse and neglect a reality, parents and professionals will have to borrow organizational lessons from advocacy groups and prevention efforts in the fields of public health, education, and mental health. With such complicated problems as child maltreatment, prevention efforts typically seek to reduce specific or predictable behaviors and problematic situations in order to promote desired outcomes. Efforts to reduce alcohol-related traffic deaths are particularly instructive in terms of how integrated an effective prevention needs to be; they involve "sensitizing the public to the hazards of driving under the influence" as well as "lobbying for lower legal blood alcohol limits, more severe penalties for offenders, innovative strategies for prevention, stricter standards on advertising of alcohol, and higher excise taxes that are designed to reduce demand for alcohol."[1]

CATEGORIES OF PREVENTIVE SERVICES

To prevent child abuse and neglect, a wide range of services and resources need to be available to parents and caregivers, children, neighborhoods, and communities. These preventive strategies are commonly classified into 3 categories—primary, secondary, and tertiary—distinguished by whom they are directed toward and the amount of risk for child maltreatment in that group.

In *primary prevention*, training, resources, and policies are provided to all parents and caregivers in the general population—regardless of risk—in an attempt to enhance the general level and quality of parenting skills and behaviors. The universal focus of primary prevention is to raise awareness of the general public, service providers, and decision makers about the scope of the problems associated with child abuse and neglect. Its goal is to stop maltreatment before it starts.

In *secondary prevention*, training, resources, and policies are provided to specific groups of parents and caregivers who have been targeted as "high-risk." Its aim is to offer

173

focused services and supports to address issues that place the child and family at risk for child maltreatment. Secondary prevention includes self-help groups for parents who consider themselves at risk for maltreating their children, home visitor programs for new parents, and parent education programs for teenagers who become parents. High-risk groups include families coping with poverty, substance abuse, teenaged pregnancy, mental health problems, or disabilities.

Tertiary prevention provides treatment services to parents or caregivers who have already abused or neglected their children. Therapy, assistance with resources, home visitors, and a variety of services and supports are made available with the hope that they will prevent further maltreatment by remedying caregiving deficits and enhancing parenting skills. Specific programs include respite care for parents, treatment for abused and neglected children, crisis intervention services, and stress management training.

Parent education offered as tertiary prevention differs in informational need from those seen in primary or secondary programs since the caregivers involved in tertiary programs have already maltreated the children in their care. For physically abusive parents, group education that emphasizes impulse control and alternative methods of discipline is particularly successful; for neglectful parents, one-on-one and home-based services with individual counseling and problem-solving techniques are likely to be more effective. Programs need to be culturally sensitive and targeted to the developmental level of the caregivers. They must also be individualized and customized around the strengths and needs of those involved. For example, for churchgoing caregivers, faith-based organizations and programs may be the best solution. Neglectful parents typically need instruction in practical childcare tasks, such as diapering and feeding an infant or observing and responding to children's signals about their needs. Programs successful in preventing emotional abuse include group-based services that define nonphysical methods of discipline, emphasize the need for consistency in determining and implementing rules, and offer parents ways of demonstrating affection toward their children. At the present time, tertiary prevention of sexual abuse is highly controversial. Because of the unique aspects of how sexual abuse situations develop, most professionals would be against allowing a child who has been sexually abused to remain in the care of the sexually abusing perpetrator. **Table 12-1** lists examples of primary, secondary, and tertiary prevention programs for reducing the risk and harm of child abuse and neglect.

Table 12-1. Child Abuse Prevention Program Examples

Type of Prevention	Examples
Primary prevention (universal approaches)	— Public service announcements encouraging positive parenting — Parent education programs and support groups focusing on development and age-appropriate expectations — Family support and strengthening programs focusing on the ability of families to access existing services, resources, and support interactions among family members — Public awareness campaigns providing information on how to report suspected child maltreatment

(continued)

Table 12-1. *(continued)*

Type of Prevention	Examples
Secondary prevention (high-risk groups)	— High school parent training programs focusing on teenaged parents — Parent education programs in substance abuse treatment centers for mothers and families with young children — Parent support groups helping caregivers manage everyday stresses — Home visitation programs providing support to new mothers — Respite care for families with children with special needs
Tertiary prevention (treatment in groups where abuse and neglect are already present)	— Mental health counselors providing intensive family preservation services, available 24 hours per day for a 6- to 8-week time period — Mentor programs pairing families with stable, nonabusive families who act as "role models" and support families in crisis — Parent support groups helping transform negative traits into positive parenting behaviors — Mental health services helping improve family communication and functioning

Adapted from Thomas et al.[1]

SERVICES PROVIDED TO PARENTS THROUGH PREVENTION PROGRAMS

Clearly, parents and caregivers can benefit immensely from instruction and support services that enhance parenting skills and competence. Content, structure, and sponsoring community groups will vary from place to place. The goals for parent education and support programs include[2,3]:

— Increasing knowledge of child development and the demands involved in caregiving.

— Enhancing skill in coping with stress, including the specific stresses of raising or providing care to an infant, child, and/or adolescent.

— Enhancing parent-child bonding, emotional ties, and communication skills.

— Increasing skill in coping with the stress of caring for children with special health care needs.

— Increasing knowledge about home and child management.

— Reducing the burden of childcare.

— Accessing social and health services for all family members in need.

— Increasing knowledge of how to teach and model tolerance to children.

— Increasing quality and quantity of time spent in developmentally appropriate activities, such as playing with, talking with, and listening to children.

All parents and caregivers can benefit to some degree by having access to parenting information, especially with their first child. Prenatal coaching, home visits, and parent support programs can all be effective in enhancing caregiving. Caregivers and parents can also benefit from stress and anger management training and from positive support services that help with coping strategies and managing the stress of parenting. Extended family members can be excellent support for new parents, and when they are not available, churches, recreational facilities, social organizations, and mental health agencies can also offer general assistance and support. Additionally, prevention efforts need to be broadly constructed so that related supports such as accessible and affordable childcare are also made available to working parents, especially single or low-income parents.

Anger management should ideally be added to programs in the criminal justice and prison systems and offered to all individuals of all ages in an effort to build basic skills and help prevent them from abusing children or other adults after being released from prison. Juvenile offenders should have therapy that will deal with their problems and illustrate appropriate ways to handle stress, anger, and aggression. Because most people in the criminal justice system will return to the community and live in family units, prevention programs have the opportunity to help this high-risk group learn how to avoid mistreating others within that family. As with all forms of prevention programs, these must be delivered in a manner that is sensitive, caring, and respectful of cultural issues in order to be as effective as possible.

School-aged children and adolescents can be provided with instruction regarding positive ways to interact and communicate with others. Life skills education can be effectively integrated into the curriculum as early as kindergarten and continue through high school and beyond. Life skills education may include many topics, but those important to preventing child maltreatment include nonviolent conflict resolution, stress and anger management, resource management, effective decision making, effective interpersonal communication, substance abuse prevention, and information regarding child development and guidance. Additionally, schools can provide a model for positive discipline practices by using consistent discipline that avoids physical force.[3]

Communities serious about child abuse prevention should make parent education classes part of a comprehensive adult education program accessible to as many parents as possible. Individuals and social institutions need to encourage parents and caregivers to seek help and build parenting skills, and they also need to work to remove any possible stigma or sense of embarrassment associated with admitting that one needs help with parenting. Parent education classes might address principles of child development, positive disciplinary techniques that avoid physical force, and childcare basics like child nutrition and safety. One vital topic from which all parents can benefit is how to enjoy caring for children. Becoming aware of techniques to improve the parent-child interaction by focusing on child development, appropriate expectations, and practical how-to-play skills can enhance both this interaction and caregivers' pleasure in their caregiving role.

Even what starts out as mild physical force associated with corporal punishment can easily turn abusive when administered by parents who are angry and under stress. To avoid this risk, parents and caregivers can learn positive methods for consistently applying discipline that do not rely on physical force. Additionally, parents need to develop constructive methods of coping with stress.

PREVENTION APPROACHES FOR SPECIFIC FORMS OF CHILD MALTREATMENT

PREVENTION OF PHYSICAL ABUSE

Among the most common causes of physical abuse are highly stressful family environments, ongoing violence, and limited access to financial and social resources. Physical abuse is most common when families experience either chronic (constant) stressors, such as poor living conditions and relationship problems, or acute (sudden/short-term) stressors, such as job loss, a death, or a new infant. A lack of access to social resources may also cause physical abuse. Prevention efforts focus on the appropriate management of available resources and supporting the development of good problem-solving skills.

When a parent or caregiver is battling mental health issues, prevention efforts typically include treatment and therapy services for all members of the family, as everyone may be affected depending on the type and intensity of the mental health disorder. Treatment and therapy support family members in learning new interpersonal communication skills and developing stronger self-esteem. The caregivers then need classes on life skills and parenting to help them increase resources and reduce stressors. Because physical abuse is common in families where one or both of the parents or caregivers is a substance abuser, it is essential to address the substance abuse issues in order to decrease the risk for child maltreatment.

Reducing chronic family stressors typically involves some component of the family's financial situation. Education and training for jobs that pay a living wage are often the beginning steps. Communities are encouraged to make sure affordable housing, childcare, health care, and transportation are available to individuals at all income levels. Families that make a living wage may need training and assistance in financial management and practical problem solving, along with job training and skill development. Families at any income level may make poor decisions and fail to recognize the relationship between their decisions and life stressors.

Substituting consistent disciplinary techniques that avoid the physical force for corporal punishment has increasingly become a focus of child maltreatment prevention efforts. People are realizing that child abuse may occur if parents use corporal punishment when they are stressed or angry. Many professionals are concerned that corporal punishment correlates with a variety of behavioral problems in children, including aggression, delinquency, low self-esteem, depression, and emotional and behavioral problems.[4] Children who experience corporal punishment may learn to use physical force as a problem-solving technique. When parents and caregivers become aware of the negative impacts associated with corporal punishment, they tend to be open to learning alternative methods of consistent and effective discipline. Adopting nonviolent forms of discipline may have both short-term and long-term benefits. In the short term, more positive forms of discipline may improve children's behavior and avoid taking the risk that physical force will get out of hand. In the long term, positive disciplinary techniques may provide children with an appropriate role model of how to interact with and influence others without the use of physical force.[5]

PREVENTION OF SEXUAL ABUSE

Sexual abuse prevention programs, to be effective, require a comprehensive strategy that teaches children how to protect themselves from sexual abuse, teaches adults how to recognize potential victims and suspicious behavior from actual or potential perpetrators, and deals with institutional and community issues that impact how sexual abuse of children is viewed and handled. The major responsibility for prevention of child sexual abuse cannot be placed solely on the victims or potential victims, since the victims are, after all, only children. Instead, programs need to educate adults on the existence of the problem, how to recognize potential victims, and on how to be supportive to the child should abuse be occurring. Prevent Child Abuse America (PCA America) continues to lead the way with effective programs for child abuse prevention including the prevention of child sexual abuse.[2] Comprehensive and effective prevention strategies often include the following:

— Provision of quality sex education, including healthy sexuality, during the pre-teenaged and teenaged years enhances knowledge of what activity is normal and what should be reported.

— Training for professionals and volunteers who work with children teaches how to identify and help children who are being abused, how to teach children to protect themselves from abuse, and how to identify those who may become potential molesters.

— Quality education for new parents provides support to enhance early attachment and bonding when their first child is born. This education should include information about appropriate and inappropriate touch and what to do about it. Parents must know how to detect and handle the sexual abuse of their own children, specifically, how to interpret symptoms that may indicate that sexual abuse has occurred.

— Institutional changes ensure that all child-serving institutions and programs (eg, schools, boys and girls clubs, childcare) train children in self-awareness and self-protection.

— Guidelines and regulations screen, train, supervise, and monitor all volunteers and staff working with children and youths.

— Treatment services are available for all victims and perpetrators of sexual abuse at potentially stressful times.

— Media messages are designed to create an environment in which the prevention programs and concepts outlined above will be effective by communicating these messages:

  — To adolescents and adults:

    — Child sexual abuse is a crime.

    — Help is available.

    — Abuse is a chronic problem unless you get help.

    — Children get hurt when you sexually abuse them.

    — Children cannot consent to sexual activity with adults or older youths.

  — To children:

    — It is okay to say "No" and run away.

    — Sexual abuse is not your fault.

    — Reach out for help if it happens to you.

    — Help is available for you; ask someone you trust.

It is essential to recognize that all victims need to receive treatment, especially since some sexual abuse perpetrators are former victims. In addition, all convicted perpetrators should receive treatment in prison or while on probation to prevent them from abusing again. Perpetrators who refuse to participate in prison treatment programs in a meaningful way should be denied their right to return to full community participation. Treatment must include individual, group, and family therapy. It is not just the victim who needs to be helped—the entire family needs help to improve their interpersonal relationships, to learn respect for the privacy of others, and to learn about each other's stress management techniques and communication skills.

PREVENTION OF EMOTIONAL ABUSE

Because emotional abuse often occurs as a precursor to other forms of child abuse and neglect and continues along with them, communities need to emphasize family support, education, and treatment in order to prevent the initial emotional problems from developing in a parent-child relationship. Support should be for both individuals and family units. Parents need to be aware of the harm that emotional abuse can inflict on children.

Some general efforts have been directed at educating the public on the potential for and great dangers of emotional abuse and calling attention to television's potential impact on social norms. Advocate groups, both community and professional, work to reduce the amount of violence on television and in music, including the marketing of violent toys. The goal is to educate parents and the general public in an attempt to promote nonviolence and well-being and change public and private attitudes toward these issues.

Other family support efforts include reducing socioenvironmental stress and increasing educational and employment opportunities. Changes must be made in values and priorities to shift societal emphasis from things to people and relationships. Social emphasis on interpersonal relationships would place priority on parent-child attachment. The improved attachment would encourage caregivers to pay more attention to children's ever-changing needs, developmental abilities, and unique personalities. It would also generate respect for children as people. Improving parent-child attachment and the quality of parenting prepares children to become more effective parents of the next generation. Parents should be encouraged to participate in both informal and formal support systems that enhance their self-esteem, value their attachment to their children, and support the priority they place on effective parenting.

Increasing the resources available to young parents will also decrease socioenvironmental stress. Stress resulting from a lack of resources can be alleviated through changes in workplace policies, salaries, and attitudes. Making resources available in the community, such as educational and leisure activities provided by parks and recreation departments or places of worship, can also help. Neighborhoods can provide important support for young parents by promoting attitudes that are family-friendly and concerned about the individuals with whom members live, work, and play.

PREVENTION OF NEGLECT

To prevent child neglect, parents must learn the basic skills and resources required to provide proper care for their children. Parents with limited financial and social resources may not be able to provide the adequate food, shelter, clothing, or mental, medical, and dental health care for their children. Additionally, parents need social support systems to help them in times of stress and full-time jobs that pay enough to meet basic expenses and offer medical benefits, especially as some parents lack the job skills necessary even for entry-level jobs. Therefore, financial resources are a vital aspect of a comprehensive approach to reducing the risk of neglect.

When communities are serious about preventing neglect, they need to ensure—through various public and private sector efforts—that all parents have access to the basic resources they need to care for their families. To care for children, parents must have access to decent and affordable housing; adequate medical, dental, and mental health care; nutritious food; developmentally appropriate childcare; and recreational activities for youths of all ages. For cases of neglect in which poverty is a factor, professionals and community members need to work in a culturally sensitive manner to promote economic development, to ensure that prevention efforts broadly address housing, jobs, substance abuse treatment, and family support.[6]

Another way to prevent neglect is to make sure parents are functioning at optimal levels, allowing them to focus on their children's needs. Some parents and caregivers are neglectful because of substance abuse or untreated mental health problems, and these caregivers need access to substance abuse treatment programs and mental health services. These services ideally would be subsidized for parents, either free of cost, at fees based on ability to pay, along sliding scales, or under provisions of employee insurance or employee assistance programs. Medicines for mental health care should be covered at the same reimbursement rate as other medications.

WHAT PARENTS AND CAREGIVERS CAN DO TO PREVENT ABUSE

PREVENTION IN THE COMMUNITY

The well-known organization PCA America challenges all to play a role in building strong communities that value children and families and keep children safe from child abuse. This group promotes the "Five R's" of child abuse prevention, which are designed to generate a better understanding of the role that people, on both community and professional levels, can play in keeping children safe from all forms of child maltreatment (**Table 12-2**).

Table 12-2. The 5 R's of Child Abuse Prevention

Raise the issue
— Stay informed and encourage politicians, your school district, and faith communities to sponsor prevention efforts such as classes and support groups for families.

Reach out to children and families in our communities
— Support children and families by being a good neighbor, helping where you can by babysitting or donating resources such as clothing, furniture, and toys to those who need them, especially young families.

Remember the risk factors
— Although child abuse and neglect crosses all groups in our society, the following are correlated risk factors:
— Substance abuse
— Isolation from support
— Anger and poor coping strategies
— Disinterest in the child's care
— Serious economic, housing, or other personal problems

(continued)

Table 12-2. *(continued)*

Recognize the warning signs
— Potential signs that may warn of possible child abuse are recognized when the child displays the following behaviors:
  — Excessive anxiety when around adults
  — Aggressiveness toward others
  — Restlessness or difficulty concentrating
  — Sudden or dramatic changes in behavior
  — Excessive interest for age in sex and/or sexually acting out
  — Unexplained or excessive bruising or other injuries
  — Low self-esteem
  — Poor hygiene, clothing inappropriate for climate, or poor nutrition

Report suspected child abuse and neglect
— Suspected child abuse should be reported to the local child protective services agency or police department. People are encouraged to call the National Child Abuse Hotline at 1-800-4-A-CHILD or another community hotline.

Data from USDHHS et al.[7]

PREVENTION IN THE HOME

Paying attention to children's emotional and psychological well-being starts with the parents and the home environment. Prevention through child education is an effective technique that everyone can practice. Parents may feel uneasy starting discussions about abuse, fearing that children will be frightened, but the list of things parents need to know how to do (**Table 12-3**) should empower them to make the right decision. Consider approaching the discussion as if teaching children general hygiene or safety rules. By discussing abuse as part of ongoing health and safety training, children will accept the information as a routine learning topic rather than as a terror-provoking "lecture."

Before sitting down with them to talk about personal safety, there are several things to consider.[8] Determine your own level of knowledge and comfort in discussing this topic. Be prepared to use language that matches children's age and level of understanding, and provide explanations of terms they do not understand. Have available any books or other materials that may be helpful during the discussion. Choose a time when children are well rested, appear receptive to talking, and when no one is rushed. Pick a place that is private and relatively free from distractions and interruptions. Also, consider the list in **Table 12-4**, which can be used as a "lesson plan" of things to discuss.

Ask children what they know about safety, including what steps to take in case of fire, if lost, or when crossing the street. Also, ask if they know any rules about personal body safety, such as different kinds of touches. Touching ranges from good touches that one

Table 12-3. What Parents Need to Know How to Do

— Listen to children

— Believe children

— Build children's self-esteem with love, praise, and attention

— Supervise children at all times

— Give children the power of information

— Recognize behavioral indicators of abuse in children

— Find community resources to help children

Table 12-4. What Children Need to Know How to Do
— Be safe
— Protect their own bodies
— Say "no" in a serious voice
— Refuse touches
— Trust their own judgment
— Tell an adult
— Be believed
— Not keep secrets
— Walk in a confident manner
— Break rules to protect themselves
— Not talk to strangers
— Refuse bribes

likes, such as hugs and kisses from a parent or holding hands with a friend, to confusing touches that make a person feel confused or uncomfortable, to inappropriate or hurtful touches that one wants to stop. Inappropriate or hurtful touches include hitting, slapping, kicking, or touches to private parts. It is important to tell children that sometimes people break personal safety rules and that child abuse does happen.[8]

Encourage children to trust their intuition, the "funny feeling" that they often get when something seems wrong but they are not sure what it is. This ability to sense danger is often experienced as a physical sensation, though children may not talk about it because they do not have the words to describe it. Professionals who work in the field of child abuse prevention have come to appreciate this sense in children. The concept of a child listening to his or her "inner voice," "uh-oh feeling," or "funny feeling" is now a part of many prevention programs. Generally children can identify with the "uh-oh" feeling when an adult describes it. Prevention begins by assuring them that these feelings exist and should be trusted. Often, little in children's experience tells them that these feelings are of value, so it is important to validate this concept for children.[8]

Teach children to trust their sense of body space. Everyone has personal boundaries that mark off body space. Depending on the relationship between 2 given people, the boundary changes. It may be at arm's length with a work associate but virtually nonexistent with a loved one. Most people can sense when someone crosses into their personal space, children included. Naming and discussing this intuitive sense of body space encourages children to trust their own feelings.[8]

Also teach children personal body rights.[8] Let them know that they have the right to choose who touches them and who does not. Think about this if you find yourself insisting that your child kiss or hug a family friend or unfamiliar relative. These situations can undermine children's belief in their own body rights. Telling a child to "kiss Aunt Jane goodbye or you'll hurt her feelings" takes away the child's right to choose. Telling children to "do what adults tell you" or permitting unwanted affection or touches from other people makes them vulnerable to abuse. Consider asking children how they would like to express respect or affection for a person. In the example of Aunt Jane, a child may feel more comfortable shaking hands or just waving goodbye.

Develop a safety plan with children in case they receive an inappropriate touch or are exposed to a sexual situation. A simple safety plan involves a child taking the following 3 actions[8]:

1. Saying "No!" using an assertive or "important" voice

2. Leaving as soon as possible

3. Telling a trusted adult about the experience as soon as possible

Practice this plan of action with children, including using their "important" voice, which should be strong and serious. An assertive voice does not have to be a yell to be effective, just decisive and forceful.[8]

Help children identify adults in their surroundings (home, school, neighborhood, church, synagogue) to turn to for help. Let them know that if the first person they tell about an inappropriate or sexual touch does not believe it, they should tell someone else and keep on telling until someone believes and helps.[8]

After the discussion, listen to children's questions and thoughts. Practice listening to them, even when the subject is uncomfortable. Show children that it is okay to tell you anything, even if they feel embarrassed or ashamed.

COST-BENEFIT ANALYSIS OF PREVENTION

When determining the costs and benefits associated with services and programs for child maltreatment, "responding costs" are those associated with low-weight births, preventable infant deaths, child deaths, medical treatment, child protective services, foster care, juvenile and adult criminal matters, and the mental health services that the victims require for their recovery. The estimated responding cost of child abuse and neglect in Michigan was $823 million in 1 year; in Colorado, associated responding costs were approximately $402 million annually.[1] Prevention services, on the other hand, were estimated to be much less. Providing prevention services to all first-time parents in Michigan for a comparable period were estimated to be $43 million and prevention-oriented home visits directed at high-risk families in Colorado would have only cost $24 million for 1 year.[1] This staggering difference between the cost of dealing with the problem after it happens and the cost of preventing it certainly support the view that prevention services have a high degree of cost effectiveness and are well worth the investment.

CHANGES IN SOCIAL INSTITUTIONS

THE ROLE OF GOVERNMENT

Because children lack the maturity and judgment to protect themselves, they must turn to adults, their family, and the community at large for protection. The community can provide protection largely via institutions such as government and religious institutions. Comprehensive child maltreatment prevention includes action taken within the judicial system. The judicial system—criminal, civil, and juvenile courts—supports laws and procedures to ensure the protection of children and support of families. Laws and judicial procedures should be sensitive to the needs and special circumstances of children. Each community should have active child advocacy groups to continually monitor the effectiveness of the legal and protective service systems.

THE ROLE OF THE MEDIA

The media (television, radio, movies, music, newspapers, and magazines) are omnipresent in our lives and as such must play a key role in the prevention of child maltreatment. Through responsible programming choices, the media can help reverse the current trend toward social and individual desensitization to the horrors of violence. As the acceptance and glamorization of violence are removed, it will be possible for all to see that violence in any form is inappropriate. The media can then replace violence with programs that depict nonviolent methods of conflict resolution. The media have been involved in educating the public about the magnitude and consequences of violence in the lives of families. They also need to teach possible alternatives to domestic violence and advocate policies beneficial to children and families. One important step the media can take is portraying parenting as an important and valued role in society.[9,10]

CONCLUSION

The resources, education, and services needed for effective parenting should be available to all caregivers, friends, family, and neighbors committed to supporting and assisting children. A comprehensive multidisciplinary approach to prevention is necessary, as is a mix of family support programs in both private and public sectors. No specific program or plan will work for all parents. Families need the informal support of extended family and friends in neighborhoods where people feel connected to each other. Neighbors must not accept abuse as "none of their business." Prevention requires society's commitment to the welfare of children, and this commitment must be backed by both governmental and private organizations and extend beyond mere rhetoric and into actual action. Actions include allocating resources for prevention initiatives and changing existing policies that do not promote child welfare. Society must recognize the importance of parenting and commit to assisting parents and other caregivers in succeeding at this challenging and rewarding job.

REFERENCES

1. Thomas D, Leicht C, Hughes C, Madigan A, Dowell K. *Emerging Practices in the Prevention of Child Abuse and Neglect.* Washington, DC: US Dept of Health & Human Services; 2003. Available at: http://www.childwelfare.gov/preventing/programs/whatworks/report/report.pdf. Accessed August 10, 2006.

2. Daro D. *Confronting Child Abuse: Research for Effective Program Design.* New York, NY: Free Press; 1998.

3. Daro D, McCurdy K. Preventing child abuse and neglect: programmatic interventions. *Child Welfare.* 1998;73:405-430.

4. Straus MA. *Beating the Devil out of Them: Corporal Punishment in American Families.* New York, NY: Lexington Books; 1994.

5. Crittenden PM, Ainsworth, MDS. Child abuse and neglect and attachment theory. In: Cicchetti D, Carlson V, eds. *Child Maltreatment: Theory and Research on the Causes and Consequences of Child Abuse and Neglect.* New York, NY: Cambridge University Press; 1989:432-463.

6. Fortin A, Chamberland C. Preventing the psychological abuse and neglect of children. *J Interpers Violence.* 1995;10:275-295.

7. US Department of Health & Human Services, National Clearinghouse on Child Abuse and Neglect Information, Prevent Child Abuse America. *Gateways to Prevention: What Everyone Can Do to Prevent Child Abuse.* Chicago, Ill: Prevent Child Abuse America; 2003. Available at: http://nccanch.acf.hhs.gov/topics/prevention/order/packet2004.pdf. Accessed June 28, 2006.

8. McNeese V, Henderson T. Talking to children. In: Monteleone JA. *A Parent's & Teacher's Handbook on Identifying and Preventing Child Abuse.* St. Louis, Mo: GW Medical Publishing; 1998:73-90.

9. US Advisory Board on Child Abuse and Neglect. *Agenda for Action. The Continuing Child Protection Emergency: A Challenge to the Nation.* Washington, DC: US Government Printing Office; 1993.

10. US Advisory Board on Child Abuse and Neglect. *Neighbors Helping Neighbors: A New National Strategy for the Protection of Children.* Washington, DC: US Government Printing Office; 1993

Appendix: Resources

APPENDIX

GENERAL RESOURCES

Childhelp

800-4-A-CHILD (800-442-4453)

http://www.childhelpusa.org

— Dedicated to the treatment, prevention, and research of child abuse and neglect by providing programs that directly serve children and their families.

— Runs the National Child Abuse Hotline 800-4-A-CHILD.

Child Welfare Information Gateway

800-394-3366

http://www.childwelfare.gov

— Promotes safety, permanency, and well-being of children and families by connecting the public and professionals to essential information on child and family safety, including abuse.

— Created through the merging of the National Clearinghouse on Child Abuse and Neglect Information and the National Adoption Information Clearinghouse.

International Child Abuse Network

888-224-4226

http://www.yesican.org

— Follows the mission statement "Working world-wide to break the cycle of child abuse."

National Youth Crisis Hotline

800-442-HOPE (800-442-4673)

— Provides 24-hour counseling and referrals to any youth in crisis, including those who are abused.

Parents Anonymous

909-621-6184

http://www.parentsanonymous.org

— Dedicated to strengthening families and building communities that promote safe, nurturing homes for children.

Prevent Child Abuse America

312-663-3520

http://www.preventchildabuse.org

— Builds awareness, provides education, and inspires hope in an effort to prevent child abuse and neglect, targeting both families and professionals.

— Promotes and implements prevention efforts at national and local levels.

— Has network of 40 state chapters.

SPECIALIZED RESOURCES

Al-Anon/Alateen
888-4AL-ANON (888-425-2666)

http://www.al-anon.alateen.org

— Supports friends and family members of alcoholics trying to recover from living with or being close to someone with a drinking problem.

— The program is adapted from the Alcoholics Anonymous 12 Steps, 12 Traditions, and 12 Concepts.

Alcoholics Anonymous
http://www.alcoholics-anonymous.org

— Provides fellowship to persons with alcoholism who wish to stop drinking; members share experiences at meetings and strive to follow a 12-step program to quit.

— Programs are nonprofessonal, self-supporting, and available almost everywhere.

— Nonalcoholics, including persons with drug addictions, may attend open meetings; only persons with a drinking problem may attend closed meetings.

American Academy of Child and Adolescent Psychiatry
202-966-7300

http://www.aacap.org

— Dedicated to treating and improving the lives of children and families with mental, behavioral, or developmental disorders.

— Credible Internet resource for children looking for information on mental health–related topics.

American Academy of Pediatrics
847-434-4000

http://www.aap.org

— Organization of pediatricians dedicated to the physical, mental, and social health of children.

— Credible Internet resource for children seeking information on health-related topics.

American Art Therapy Association
888-290-0878

http://www.arttherapy.org

— Promotes the therapeutic use of art by providing standards of professional competence and providing knowledge in and of the field of art therapy.

Art Therapy Credentials Board
877-213-2822

http://www.atcb.org

— Qualifies art therapists as registered and/or board certified.

Boys & Girls Clubs of America
800-854-CLUB (to find your local club)

http://www.bgca.org

— Provides programs and services that enhance the development of boys and girls by instilling a sense of competence, usefulness, belonging, and influence.

— Neighborhood-based buildings are open every day, employ professionals trained in youth development, and have extremely low yearly dues so that all children may participate.

Break the Cycle
888-988-TEEN (888-988-8336)

http://www.break-the-cycle.org

— Educates and empowers youths to build lives and communities free from domestic and dating violence.

Can We Talk?
202-822-7570

http://www.canwetalk.org

— Parent education program that helps bridge the gap that exists between schools, parents, children, and difficult topics such as sexuality and health.

Channing Bete Company
800-477-4776

http://www.channing-bete.com

— Provides educational and awareness materials to schools, organizations, businesses, and government agencies.

Child Care Aware
800-424-2246 or 866-278-9428

http://childcareaware.org

— Provides articles, tips, publications, and glossaries on childcare, as well as online calculators and evaluation guidelines to help parents choose a provider.

CyberTipline of the National Center for Missing & Exploited Children
800-THE-LOST (800-843-5678)

http://www.cybertipline.com

— Reporting mechanism for Internet exploitation, including child pornography, online enticement, molestation, sex tourism, prostitution of children, and unsolicited obscene material sent to children.

Family Violence Prevention Fund
415-252-8900

http://endabuse.org

— Works toward ending violence against women and children around the world by reaching all audiences (including men and youths), promoting leadership in communities, and transforming the way professionals view violence.

Good Touch/Bad Touch®
800-245-1527

http://www.goodtouchbadtouch.com

— Curriculum for children and training for educators and professionals about the identification, treatment, and prevention of child sexual abuse.

— Created by a mother of children being sexually abused without her knowledge.

KidsHealth
http://www.kidshealth.org

— Provides doctor-approved health information to both adults and children.

The Kids on the Block
800-368-KIDS (800-368-5437)

http://www.kotb.com

— Program using puppets and scripts to address various disabilities, including educational and medical differences, and social concerns such as sexual abuse.

Narcotics Anonymous
818-773-9999

http://www.na.org

— Provides fellowship and support for drug addicts wishing to overcome their addiction and live drug-free lives.

— Members following the program of 12 Steps and 12 Traditions meet and share the successes and challenges they experience.

National AfterSchool Association (formerly the National School-Age Care Alliance)
800-617-8242

http://www.naaweb.org

— Develops, accredits, and approves after-school programs for young children and middle schoolers.

National Association for the Education of Young Children
800-424-2460

http://www.naeyc.org

— Works to make quality educational and developmental services available to all children from birth to 8 years of age.

— Provides information on early childhood education and development to parents, teachers, and students, in addition to accrediting programs and hosting an annual conference.

National Association for Family Child Care
800-359-3817

http://www.nafcc.org

— Accredits childcare providers and allows parents to search for them online.

National Coalition Against Domestic Violence
303-839-1852

http://www.ncadv.org

— Works for the major societal changes necessary to eliminate both personal and social violence against all women and children.

— Advocates coalition building, the creation of community-based safe homes and shelters, education, and legislation.

The National Center for Victims of Crime
202-467-8700

http://www.ncvc.org

— Helps victims of crime rebuild their lives by providing direct services and resources, advocating for laws, training professionals, and promoting new ways of thinking about victims.

The National Child Care Information Center
800-616-2242

http://www.nccic.org

— Functions as a national clearinghouse on all information related to child health and education.

— Run by the federal Child Care Bureau, it links resources and information for and from parents, childcare providers, policy makers, research, and the public.

National Domestic Violence Hotline
800-799-SAFE (800-799-7233)

http://www.ndvh.org

— Hotline providing 24-hour crisis intervention, safety planning, information, and referrals to agencies.

National Education Association
202-833-4000

http://www.nea.org

— Volunteer-based organization that provides a voice for education professionals and works toward providing great public schools for all children.

National Sexual Violence Resource Center
877-739-3895

http://www.nsvrc.org

— Collects and disseminates a wide range of resources on sexual violence to assist coalitions, advocates, and others interested in understanding and eliminating sexual violence.

Net Nanny
http://www.netnanny.com

— Provides software and Web-based safety solutions for parents to help keep children safe on the Internet.

Netsmartz

http://www.netsmartz.org

— Teaches children how to stay safe on the Internet through interactive activities, including lessons on how to recognize dangers, understand that people on the Internet are strangers, and report victimization.

Outward Bound

845-424-4000

http://www.outwardbound.org

— Offers people of all ages outdoor adventure programs structured to build team-working skills, confidence, and independence and encourage the development of character, compassion, and a desire to improve the self and world.

PANdora's Box: The Secrecy of Child Sexual Abuse

http://www.prevent-abuse-now.com

— Advocates for the protection of children and the prevention of child sexual abuse.

A Parent's Guide to Internet Safety (FBI Publication)

http://www.fbi.gov/publications/pguide/pguidee.htm

— Publication that teaches parents about the complexities of online child exploitation.

Red Cross

202-303-4498

http://www.redcross.org

— Reliable resource for parents looking for specific information on safety or babysitter training.

Safe Child

http://www.safechild.org

— Curriculum that works to protect children from bullying, abuse, and abduction.

Safekids.com and Safeteens.com

http://www.safekids.com
http://www.safeteens.com

— Web sites created for children and teenagers to teach about the general risks of Internet use.

Staysafe.org

http://www.staysafe.org

— Helps consumers understand the positive aspects of the Internet and the safety and security issues that exist there.

— Different areas target all different age groups.

V-Day

http://www.vday.org

— Global movement to stop violence against women and girls by staging large-scale benefits and producing innovative gatherings, films, and campaigns to educate and change social attitudes about violence.

Index

Quickly find information about medical aspects of child abuse when and where it is needed

For professionals working with children, the tremendous amount of information concerning child maltreatment can be difficult to retain. The completely revised and expanded *Child Abuse Quick Reference* is designed to provide these busy professionals with the information they need to recognize children at high risk for abuse and neglect and rapidly diagnose child maltreatment.

The chapters address the most common types of child abuse as well as uncommon but possible causes such as cultural or religious practices that often look like abuse. The format is arranged to identify an issue, describe methods of assessment and treatment, point out essentials of investigation and prosecution, and summarize education and prevention strategies.

Knowledge is the best weapon against child abuse and this book helps elevate the understanding of those individuals working on the front line, making them better equipped to confront the challenges they face daily, and be instruments of positive change for the health and well-being of children and their familes.

Child Abuse *Quick Reference Second Edition*
For Health Care, Social Service, and Law Enforcement
Angelo P. Giardino, MD, PhD, MPH, FAAP;
Randell Alexander, MD, PhD, FAAP
448 Pages, 150 images, 93 contributors
ISBN 10:1-878060-60-0 ISBN 13:978-1-878060-60-0

$46.95

Protect children by helping them make wise decisions on their own

Child Safety calls upon the knowledge of expert pediatricians to empower those who care for children. This guide addresses ques-tions that arise throughout a child's develop-ment with discussions on topics ranging from child safety in the home to the timely issue of terrorism.

Reviewed by an advisory board of parents and child advocates, *Child Safety* is written in language that is easy to understand and accessible to all caregivers. Readers can easily access information using tables and check-lists designed to highlight important issues.

This affordable resource is an important tool for combating safety and health risks and equipping caregivers with the information they need to protect their children and teach them to make wise decisions on their own.

Child Safety
A Pediatric Guide for Parents, Teachers,
Nurses, and Caregivers
Angelo P. Giardino, MD, PhD MPH, FAAP;
Cynthia W. DeLago, MD; Hans B. Kersten, MD;
Paul S. Matz, MD; Robert S. McGregor, MD;
Laura E. Smals, MD; Nancy D. Spector, MD
250 Pages, 60 images, 10 contributors
ISBN 10:1-878060-67-8 ISBN 13:978-1-878060-67-9

$23.00